FAMILY FIELDS
Eight Generations Living in the Country

ROBERT SIMPER

Published in 1999 by Creekside Publishing

ISBN 0 9519927 9 1
Printed by Lavenham Press

By the same author

Over Snape Bridge (1967)
Woodbridge & Beyond (1972)
East Coast Sail (1972)
Scottish Sail (1974)
North East Sail (1975)
British Sail (1977)
Victorian & Edwardian Yachting from Old Photographs (1978)
Gaff Sail (1979)
Traditions of East Anglia (1980)
Suffolk Show (1981)
Britain's Maritime Heritage (1982)
Sail on the Orwell (1982)
Beach Boats of Britain (1984)
Sail: The Surviving Tradition (1984)
East Anglian Coast and Waterways (1985)
Suffolk Sandlings (1986)
The Deben River (1992)
The River Orwell and the River Stour (1993)
Rivers Alde, Ore and Blyth (1994)
Woodbridge: Pictorial History (1995)
Essex Rivers and Creeks (1995)
Norfolk Rivers and Harbours (1996)
Thames Tideway (1997)
River Medway and the Swale (1998)
In Search of Sail (1998)

Contents

Burning rubbish.

Nobby Burch combining Spring barley 1975.

INTRODUCTION

The English countryside is entirely man-made, the result of around three thousand years of continual occupation. It is a strong characteristic of human beings that they cannot leave anything unchanged. If there are trees they will cut them down, if there are no trees they will plant some. When you look at the countryside you are viewing the dreams and ambitions of the countless generations of countrymen who have either reshaped the landscape or given up in desperation. The story of how the modern villages have been shaped is well chronicled in countless books. Those on East Anglia which stand out are Spike May's *Reuben's Corner*, George Ewart Evans' *Ask The Fellow Who Cuts The Hay* and then Ronald Blythe's *Akenfield*. Adrian Bell with *Corduroy* and others in his trilogy on farming recorded the working life of yeoman farmers. Since then there have been profound changes in the countryside and 'the farmer' is often portrayed as a stranger, usually viewed from over the hedge with a purely urban perspective.

My intention with this book is not just to write about my own farming career, or even the history of my family over the past two hundred years, but to use our combined stories to describe the events which have shaped the East Anglian countryside.

Most of this book has been written in the evenings, having returned home after a day organising the progress of huge machines, often by talking to their drivers on mobile phones, in the relentless quest to produce good quality affordable food. My working life seems totally different now. When I began, forty-six years ago, we still had horses on the farm.

Yet when I researched through the records and legends of my family over the past two hundred years I was struck, not by differences, but by the similarities. When Joshua Oxborrow went farming in the early nineteenth century his problems would have been the weather, borrowing capital from the banks, dealing with landowners and their agents and with fluctuating market prices. On top of this was the great indifference of the general public, who simply wanted to buy food as cheaply as they could get it. All these facets are still part of a farmer's working life, almost exactly the same as they were two hundred years ago.

What has gone out of farming is the drudgery. Really this went with the horses and my family fought very hard to get away from the life of working seven days a week in endless muck and mud. There was a lot of brute force and ignorance about the old farming practices, working conditions were hard on men and harder still on animals and there was a surprising disregard for the environment.

It is very difficult to do a detailed history of every field, farm and village because most of the past is quickly forgotten. All we find in the land of the people that came before us are old horseshoes and sheeps' bells and all we leave are worn power harrow tines and broken shear bolts. But every part of the countryside goes through the same period, so by following one family it is possible to catch a glimpse of the land as it has changed.

Although I have written about my family using their Christian names I never used these when they were still around. In fact, with grandmothers I was not even aware of their names until I went to their funerals. The surname Simper is believed to have derived from those who came over with William the Conqueror from St Pierre in Normandy. The arrival out of the blue of Michael Simper's *The St Pierre Newsletter* and subsequent material has helped to fill up several gaps in my knowledge of my own family. The stronghold of this name, which crops up all over England, appears to be Suffolk, but today there are more Simpers in Utah than anywhere else!

In trying to piece together this unique story of eight generations in the same occupation in the same area I naturally relied heavily on family reminiscences, particularly from Norman Simper, Philip Simper and Margaret Cole. Also Herman Simper and his daughter Carol Twinch, both well-known writers on the agricultural scene. On the Turner side, from Lilian Simper and Jack Hewitt. My memory on recent farming matters has been considerably jogged by my son Jonathan. On a more practical front in preparing this book I have to thank my wife Pearl and Diana McMillan for editing and my daughter Caroline Southernwood for the artwork. This is my twenty-fifth book and by far the most difficult because it is so close to home.

RS
Ramsholt

Robert combining in 1995.

Two horses in a lane,

Chapter One

WALKING TO CHAPEL

ALL TIMES IS PAST
AND SO IS MINE
Anglo-Saxon saying

I was about ten years old when my mother had to go into hospital for a long time and Great Aunt Kate came to look after Father and myself. I had never met her before and am afraid I rather resented the old lady coming into our home and taking over. As a small boy, used to roaming freely around the farm, I did not take kindly to Kate's Victorian standards of discipline. She was a rather strait-laced 'maiden aunt', an old term meaning she had never married, and I am sure she lived up to this term in every way. Kate had been brought up in a small Suffolk village where very puritan values of hard work and obedience went unchallenged. Small children of her day, we were led to believe, were seen and not heard.

When I refused to go to bed fast enough she would chase me, flicking a towel against the backs of my young legs. Very painful and humiliating. It must have been in the very cold winter of 1947, because I remember snow lying on the ground during her visit. Once when she had the kitchen window open to let steam out I lobbed a snowball in and scored a direct hit on the elderly figure. I still remember the cry of surprise and pain and my own great sense of delight at scoring a small victory.

I did not really see Kate again until after my grandfather Herman's death in 1961. Then she started to reappear at family gatherings as a sort of representative of the departed and much loved head of the family. Meeting her again, I saw her in quite a different light. She was rather a kindly old lady, I suppose by then well into her eighties, and she remembered with great fondness her short period as housekeeper at Manor Farm, Bawdsey. That brief winter visit many years before was a bond between us.

One Christmas I asked Kate about our family history. She at once began to reel off names of places and people I had never heard of. She came out with statements such as 'at that time of day our people had a farm up the back of Debenham.'

I desperately tried to remember all this information, but names of relations long dead and villages they had lived in were rather a lot to take in at one sitting. However, a few weeks later a small neat parcel arrived and I discovered Kate had sent me all the family records. This amounted to not really very much, faded brown portrait photographs, a few of the farm tenancy agreements and a collection of old postcards. I planned to read all this material up and then go and see Kate to sort out who they all were, but unfortunately she died before I got round to doing this.

This small pile of documents represented the starting-point of my efforts to trace lives, difficulties and high points of one family, in this case my own, over the course of two centuries of constant strife to make a living from working the land.

I believe the family came from the villages of north Suffolk. The earliest record I have come across was for one Matthew Simper of Rickinghall Inferior in about 1636. There had been a court case, as a Simper had found some clothes missing from a chest in his barn. A labourer had been seen coming out of the barn holding a pair of trousers, however the records don't say how this court case ended. Then there was silence until 1794 when in the will of Stranger, a farmer at Thorndon, £30 was left to his daughter Ann, who was married to the weaver William Simper of Rishangles. Sounds like enough capital to have started any young man on a career in farming.

If William Simper went into farming just before the Napoleonic Wars, it was a very good piece of luck. The price of wheat during that war rose to 113 shillings a quarter (£26 a ton) and even a small piece of cultivated ground could have brought a family a living. A man with a large acreage earned a fortune.

The details of the family at this time are a little hazy. Just to confuse matters further, three generations of them had the same Christian name of Samuel. It would appear that one of the sons of Richard and Mary Simper, both born at Framsden before 1734, was a Samuel Simper. In the late eighteenth century this Samuel married Martha and they lived at Bedingfield, the next parish to Rishangles. As an old lady, Martha appears to have lived at Bedingfield with my great-great-grandparent Samuel Simper, who was born there in 1812, which suggests she was his mother. Samuel Simper appears to have farmed the 16 acre Hill Farm at Bedingfield all his life. In some records he is a labourer, which suggests his holding was not large enough to support a family, so that some of the time, probably at harvest, he worked on other farms.

Samuel Simper married Harriet Canham and both signed all official documents with their marks, so it is assumed that they could not write their names. Samuel and Harriet were keen members of the Zion Baptist chapel at Rishangles and would have walked there every Sunday to attend services.

1. George Stubbs, 'Reapers' of 1785, shows how corn was cut with sickles. To try and speed up the harvest farmers started to have barley and oats cut with scythes. Wheat was a thicker crop and it was not until the 1840s that farmers got their harvest companies to use scythes which proved quicker.

2. The Zion Baptist chapel at Rishangles in 1978. On the left Caroline, Joanna and Pearl are looking at the graves of Samuel and Harriet Simper.

In the Victorian period the non-conformist chapels were a powerful force in East Anglian villages and were strongly supported by the working people, tradesmen and small farmers. The great landowners were Church of England and would not let the non-conformists have land for a chapel, so typically the Rishangles' chapel, a huge building squeezed on a narrow piece of land between two roads, was built in the garden of a shopkeeper.

Samuel and Harriet were there when the yellow brick Baptist chapel at Rishangles was enlarged in 1862 to seat 450 people, far more than it ever needed. The Baptist version of a plain life being rewarded in heaven was shared by many people living in rural East Anglia. Not long after this Samuel was a key player in a great village row which was probably the centre of gossip in Rishangles for months, but which the outside world knew nothing about.

The chapel pastor lived at Church Farm and noticed that one of his meadows did not seem to grow any grass. Then it was pointed out to him that one of his congregation, Robert Newson, was putting his pony to graze in the meadow just after dark and getting it out before most people in the village awoke. The pastor was furious and Samuel Simper, as an elder of the chapel, was appointed to sort this matter out. A bit of investigation after dark revealed Newson's pony happily grazing in the pastor's meadow. The chapel elders met and Newson was expelled from the congregation. Hell hath no fury like Suffolk chapel people when they think they have been morally wronged!

Most of Samuel and Harriet's family left rural Suffolk and moved to London, where some of their descendants still live. Harriet died in 1877 and Samuel in 1887 and they were buried in the little graveyard beside the road at Rishangles chapel.

One member of their family who went to the London area was their eldest son, George. He was a harness-maker who moved to Canning Town in search of a better life, but only exchanged the poverty of rural Suffolk for the slums of the East End of London, where he died in great poverty in 1928.

It was one of his sons, Eric Edward, who became the variety turn 'Ernie French', and did not have a home as he toured the music halls constantly. In 1923 he was in Seattle on the west coast of the United States, having 'gone west' in the hope of making a fortune. His son Ray Simper, who later became a London policeman, remembered that there were 'native Americans' begging in the dirty streets of Seattle and he had a bad time at school because his mother sent him with a cap and short trousers, while American boys wore knickerbockers. Ernie French brought his family back to London where some of them are still working in television. Most of the Suffolk Simpers had lost contact with relations in London, but my Grandfather Herman, one Sunday afternoon sitting by the fire at Brook Farm, began talking about one of his family who had 'trod the boards'.

I asked, hoping that at least one of the family was famous, about this 'actor'. 'No, he never did any good at all on the stage', said my grandfather with a smile. I think he got pleasure from the fact that the ones in the family who had stayed working the farms had made a reasonable living, while the ones drawn to the big city, referred to as 'up the smoke', had simply been swallowed up by it.

In the Victorian period there were around thirty thousand farms in Suffolk, ranging in size from about 5 acres up to around 300 acres, mostly arable revolving around growing wheat with some cattle and a lot of sheep. Nearly all this land was owned by the large estates, many of them had been in the same family for centuries. Tenancies granted were usually just for a single year and some farmers moved around a great deal trying to find a good landlord.

Back in the 'Hungry forties' labouring families wandered the lanes, sleeping rough and looking for work. During the late-Victorian Agricultural Depression it was not quite so bad because most districts had workhouses. People no longer starved to death by the roadside, but their existence in the workhouses was degrading and brutal.

The fear of the workhouse drove the labourers, horsemen, village tradesmen and the small tenant farmers into working from dawn until dusk. The land-owning families were sometimes charitable to the villagers in need of help, but they regarded country people as being a separate race, having their own customs and talking their own dialect.

Although many small tenant farmers in heavy land Suffolk were ruined by the wet harvest of 1860, farming received a boost from the food shortages during the Crimean and then the Franco-German War, but in 1879 a series of bad harvests started, resulting in an agricultural depression which lasted until 1914. Landlords, used to high rents, refused to accept the down-turn and bankrupted their tenants, then advertised for new ones. This was the start of the drift south by Scottish farmers in search of easier land to work.

The reason grain prices started to fall was that in the 1880s the railroads linked up the north American prairies with ports. This destroyed small scale farming in the eastern United States, which has never recovered. The grain then crossed the North Atlantic to put

European farming into a depression. In British corn markets wheat dropped from just over £12 a ton down to about £6.80 per ton. Farming was pretty grim and the small farmers survived by working hard and spending less. By the late Victorian period good land which had been rented out for about £2 an acre had dropped, if a tenant could be found, to ten shillings (50p) an acre. Many villages became full of poor country people who struggled to earn a few shillings a week to live on. The families of labourers who were unsuccessful in getting work lived very near to starvation on 'parish relief'.

The British industrialists, investors and industrial workers were very happy with this arrangement. British-built ships carried out steam coal from South Wales, or manufactured goods, and returned home with grain and frozen meat. The British Government saw no point in protecting farming if food could be bought so cheaply from overseas. The countryside could then become a playground for rich townsfolk who went down to their estates to hunt the fox and shoot pheasants.

Farming during the late Victorian and Edwardian period was very volatile, with farms constantly changing hands and many of the old farming families departed for a new life in the colonies. The Samuel Simper who lies buried at Rishangles had two sons, Benjamin and Sam, who took up farming in their native county. The elder of these was Benjamin and he is described in the Kelly's Dictionaries first as a cattle dealer and later as a farmer.

Benjamin remained very loyal to the chapel at Rishangles, but farmed some two miles south at Aspall, a small hamlet just north of Debenham. He appears to have had Hill House Farm and another farm at Earl Stonham, a few miles to the west. Like most of his family, Benjamin 'reached a good age' and was eighty-nine years old when he died at Cretingham, leaving £214. My father's generation remember an Aunt Ben, who used to visit Charsfield in the 1930s. This was his second wife, Ellen, a lady nearly thirty years his junior, who he married at Rishangles chapel in 1898.

3. Street Farm, Framsden in 1978. In 1854 this 30 acre farm was increased to 42 acres, but then in the 1930s linked up with Church Farm to increase the acreage again. In about 1957 the farm was incorporated with the Helmingham Hall Estate farms.

Benjamin's son by his first wife was Fred, born in 1861, and he moved to Framsden and took the tenancy of Street Farm, a farm closely connected with my family for about one hundred and fifty years. This was very appropriate, as the farm stood almost opposite the 'Greyhound' public house and Fred's great passions were coursing greyhounds and visiting the pub. He lived to be about ninety-four, farming right to the end at Street Farm and Church Farm and every Tuesday he went to Ipswich Market. He married twice and had an adopted daughter, who became a school teacher, and left an incredible £3,352.

My first interest in these long forgotten relatives came in 1972, when I had my first proper book published. The Ancient House bookshop in Ipswich (how I miss going in there to browse around) kindly organised a signing session. When I arrived the manager said, 'one of your relations has already been in!'

I had never heard of the lady he named and was totally mystified. Shortly afterwards a small elderly lady in a fur coat returned and very proudly said she was Fred's daughter. At the time I had never heard of Fred, or 'cousin Fred' as he was known in the family, and it has taken me some twenty-five years to unravel this lady's remote connection to myself.

Samuel's youngest child was another Sam, born at Bedingfield, and he sometimes appears in the early records as a labourer and I think he worked with his elder brother Benjamin. Anyway, Sam took a fancy to Elizabeth Oxborrow, whose father Joshua Oxborrow was a tenant of Street Farm in Framsden, a village just to the south of Debenham. Valentine cards that Sam sent Elizabeth in 1872 were carefully kept and were in the parcel Great Aunt Kate sent me. More to the point, the cards helped to win the lady's heart and the following year the couple were married at Framsden Church.

Joshua Oxborrow's wife was already dead, so it seems Elizabeth was running his household. This must have continued, with Sam Simper going into partnership with seventy year-old Joshua at Street Farm, Framsden. According to a family legend, this farm tenancy had been passed down for seven generations. This is quite likely, but they were not all the Simper family. The earliest document Great Aunt Kate gave me is a hand-written family tree going back to Samuel Oxborrow of 1763 who was living in Framsden. He married Hannah and they had thirteen children. Two of these seem to have been the twins Calab and Joshua, born in 1808. Whether they were identical or not there is no way of telling, but they both stayed in the village. Calab became a shoemaker, while Joshua took on the tenancy of Street Farm.

The first definite mention of Street Farm is in an inventory of 1841. This appears to have been made on the death of Joshua Oxborrow, for his son, Joshua, took on the lease of Street Farm and still held it when he went into partnership with Sam nearly forty years later. All the 'implements' and household furniture on this 42 acre holding were valued at £280. It was a very detailed account of the holding and the impression is that farming and village life at that time were highly organised, with very clear rules about how everything was to be done. This type of farming had been going on for a long time, even then.

Joshua Oxborrow's lease of 1860 has survived and shows clearly that his landlord, Lord John Tollemache, insisted on having the maximum return from his land. The rent was pegged to the price of wheat and the landlord was taking about half the income from the farm. Wheat was then fifty-five shillings a quarter (£12 a ton) and the rent was £1.80 per acre which had to be paid in cash.

The lease showed that the barter system had only just finished. It would appear that until very recently the tenants had been paying for their farms, just as the medieval ones had done, with free labour and straw. The crossed-out clauses stated how many wagon-loads of 'good Dry Wheat Straw' had to be delivered to Helmingham Hall, no doubt for the riding stables, and how 'Days Team Work (gratis), with a wagon and four horses' have been wavered. On top of this, the tenant of Street Farm still had to give free beer to any of Tollemache's workmen while they did repairs on the property. On top of the rent, the tenant also had to pay Tithes, the tax levied by the Church of England, Highway Rates to repair the parish roads, and County Rates and Poor Rates to support the villagers who could not work.

The 1860 lease is a closely-printed document running to three pages and sets out very clearly how the tenant must farm the land up to a high standard. The farm had to be managed according to a 'four-shift Husbandry'. This was the method made popular by the eighteenth century Norfolk squire, Viscount 'Turnip' Townsend, to put fertility back into the soil. The medieval strip farming and commonland system had been a disaster, because nobody had the incentive to keep the land 'in good heart'. In the medieval period the population of England and Wales was only around three million so there was enough space for a fairly relaxed form of agriculture. However, a crop failure in any county meant a famine, in which the poor died of hunger (the Irish potato famine is the one most remembered and still influences attitudes). Famines meant riots and social unrest so the ruling classes were very keen to increase food production. By 1810, the population had grown to ten million and there was no possibility that the common field strip farming could feed the population so the land was enclosed into privately-owned fields to increase the yields, and of course the rent revenue, of the landowners.

Viscount Coke's four course or four shift crop rotation meant that in the first year land was left as uncropped fallow, in Suffolk this was called a Summerland pronounced 'Sumer'lond'. During this fallow the field would be ploughed several times in the hope of killing the weeds. Then the following year it could be barley or oats and followed by beans, which put nitrogen into the soil, or clover which was grazed by sheep. Finally, on the fourth year, wheat would be grown, the major earning crop.

After three years of building up fertility, the average yield was still under a ton an acre. The Victorian farmers also began to use artificial chemical fertilisers, Lord Tollemache's leases said clearly that artificial fertilizers had to be used to increase yields. A more important way of increasing yields was a drainage programme started in the Victorian period and lasting into the 1970s. More than anything else, land drainage has increased yields in Britain. By getting the subsoil water away the plant's roots can go down deeper and so in the summer draw up moisture and keep the plant growing.

Oxborrow's 1860 lease stated that he had to dig trenches, all done by hand, and lay a thousand tile drainage pipes in the fields every year. The Victorian land drainage pipes were mostly too small and they blocked up quite quickly. However some laid on really heavy land at Barham in the 1860s were still working in 1999.

With Street Farm, the maximum wheat area would only have been about 10 acres, and even with the four course system Oxborrow must have produced about 10 tons of wheat a year which supported him, his family and his workforce. The beans and barley gave little income because these were mainly fed to the animals. Of course there was some income from a few cattle, sheep and a pig or two. Both the Earl Stonham and Framsden land would have been 'one horse' farms and that one horse, and a small pony to pull the family's trap, would have had all their food grown on the farm. Keeping the horse fed used about a quarter of the land on most farms.

It is very difficult to work out now how these tiny farms supported so many people.

Working on 1998 prices, the output from the Framsden farm would have provided an income to pay a tractor driver for about two weeks. The whole economic situation was totally different, the truth being that in the Victorian period food prices were very high and took the major part of most families' incomes. The need to feed the population in the industrial towns cheaply was uppermost in the minds of the more responsible politicians of the nineteenth century.

Street Farm's 42 acres labour requirement comprised the farmer, two farm labourers and a young girl who worked in the house as a servant and helped on the farm in busy times. The holding was divided into thirteen enclosures, all arable fields except for the five tiny meadows on one side of the farmhouse. On the other side of the small neat brick farmhouse was a big kitchen garden. All farmers and their workers, indeed everyone in the villages, would have grown their own vegetables in their spare time. Although the country people had very little cash, so long as they were able and willing to wield garden tools they did not go hungry.

All farms had chickens scratching around the farmyard which provided eggs and meat. The farmer's wife looked after the chickens and the 'egg money' was usually her only personal income. The chickens were fed on 'dross' corn (the stuff too poor to be sold), while

4. The barn at Baylam Hall about 1905. This is typical of the larger Suffolk corn barns. The doors of the middlestead are open and no doubt the clean straw was thrown out into the pig yard so that they looked clean for their photograph. Barns built for threshing with a stick and a half had a threshing floor in the middle, but the later barns were large enough to stand a drum in. Once steam threshing started most corn was stored in stacks in the open.

the farm-worker's chickens were in theory fed on corn which had been 'gleaned' from the fields by the women. In fact there was a running battle between the farmer and his men to stop them from smuggling small amounts of wheat out of the 'corn chamber' for their own hens' consumption. The door to the farm granary or corn chamber was usually positioned so that it could be watched from the farmhouse to avoid theft.

Wheat was sold in coombe sacks and in the language of the day this was 55 shillings a quarter. The Street Farm had to be kept in 'good husbandry', which meant plenty of farm-yard muck. This way the Victorian farmers could put some nitrogen into the soil with farmyard muck and the four course system, but fields still needed potash and phosphate to increase their yields. Some phosphate could be bought by then, but they still had terrible trouble trying to increase yields to pay the rents. Also, there was an everlasting problem with weeds, which could only be controlled by making a fallow, ploughing or hand-harrowing. On a wet year, the weeds grew faster than they could be hand-hoed and would sometimes swamp the crop.

The cereal crops were cut with a horse-drawn binder during the August harvest and stored in the small barn. During the winter months, the crop was threshed with a flail, known as a 'stick and a half' in Suffolk. The two doors on either side of the barn were opened so that air blew through and helped to separate the chaff from the straw. The grain kernels remained on the hard clay floor from where they were shovelled into coombe sacks which were carried by the men on their backs up the steps to the tiny granary at the back of Street Farmhouse. In an age of dirt floors, the grain was normally stored on a second floor, and to prevent stealing it was almost always stored in or near the farmhouse.

The few family stories that have come down from that Victorian era make no mention of the Tollemache family, but tales still live on about that era in Framsden village. Lord John's estate covered most of Ashbocking, Pettaugh, Gosbeck and Framsden and on this estate all tenants had to show respect to Lord and Lady Tollemache, dress according to their station in life and attend church on Sundays.

John Tollemache had inherited the Helmingham Hall Estate in 1841 from his great aunt Louisa, Countess of Dysart. This inheritance included land all over the country, but Lord John Tollemache made Framsden and Helmingham the showpiece of this great estate and built model cottages for his workers there. The principle house on this estate was Helmingham Hall, a wonderful Elizabethan moated mansion surrounded by 400 acres of parkland which was also the home of 700 deer.

Lord John rode around on horseback, very much lord of all he surveyed, and supervised all the building work he put in hand. In his Model Village he built workers' cottages in a 'Tollemache Tudor' style. He insisted his cottage tenants all kept a pig, which of course was fed on household scraps (if any) and food the women 'gleaned', by picking up loose crop-ears of cereal crops after the corn had been carted to the barn. At the end of the year the pig was killed and sold to pay the cottage rent. The cottagers all had about half an acre of land and on this Lord John insisted they grew their own food.

Providing you remembered to touch your hat to the great lord, then the estate system worked well enough. Certainly in the Victorian period most people preferred to live in a 'closed' village where the housing was a great deal better than the rural slums in some 'open' villages of small landowners, where leaking rooves and broken windows were com-mon.

The great estates were building new cottages, and in the old houses dirt floors were replaced with wooden ones. Some farmhouses had, from the previous century, brick floors

5. A boy bringing two Suffolk horses back from a day's harrowing at Rendlesham in 1903.

in the herringbone pattern. The practice of putting straw, swept up once a week, on the kitchen floor to catch the mud brought in from the farmyard lasted in some remote farm-houses until after World War II. The other great improvement on the nineteenth century was the coal-burning kitchen range replacing the open hearth, while the brick privy at the bottom of the garden became a standard feature.

The 'mixed' arable and livestock farms of East Anglia fed the farmer and his family and provided 'fuel' for his horses to work the land. The sale of wheat and a few fat cattle, sheep and pigs left enough over to pay the landlord and the men's wages. The living standard of the tenant farmer, even on a tiny acreage, was far better than that endured by his labourer.

The Oxborrows were tenants on the Helmingham Hall Estate for a long time. Like their landlords, the Oxborrows were Church of England, but Sam Simper had a strong leaning towards the non-conformist chapel. Being marked as a 'chapel-goer' would not have helped his progress to get a tenancy on the Tollemache's Estate, and maybe that is why Sam moved away. Although other members of the family came back on the estate, they were Church of England.

After Sam and Elizabeth Simper and their family left Framsden, they moved from farm to farm around east Suffolk. Their sons worked on the family farm from an early age, for nothing but their keep. Their first son was Horace, born in 1877 and he eventually took the tenancy of Bond's Corner Farm, Grundisburgh, but life as a slave to the land did not suit him. He became a policeman at Mildenhall and then moved to Canning Town in the East

The Sowers.

6. Broadcasting cereal seed by hand followed by a horse harrowing in the seed, 1904. Most of the larger farms had Smythe coulter drills, but broadcasting was still done on some farms. Grass seed was still broadcast by hand into the 1950s.

7. The Witnesham Chapel outing at Witnesham Hall in 1903. Sam Simper in the bowler hat is sitting to the left of the man with a tray.

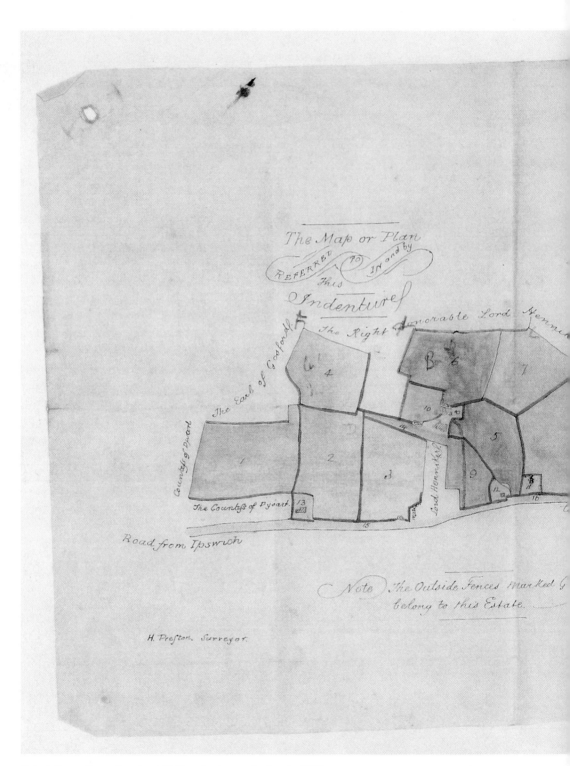

Potash Farm, Framsden about 1840 and sales particulars in 1936.

No	Fields Names &c	Contents		
		a	r	p
1	Upper Field	4	0	2
2	Neathouse Field	3	1	35
3	Skeets Meadow	3	1	1
4	Cats do	2	2	0
5	Home do	2	0	18
6	Backhouse do	3	0	7
7	Hopyard Piece	3	0	2
8	Mill Field	5	0	30
9	Road Field	1	1	6
10	Yards Orchard &c	1	0	17
11	Mill Premises		1	0
12	Potash Cottages &c	"	"	30
13	Low Cottage &c	"	1	15
14	Lane			38
15	Moiety of Road	"	1	20
	Total A	30	1	19

Lord Henniker

Soham.

Framsden and Ashfield

SUFFOLK

Particulars and Conditions of Sale

OF A WELL-SITUATED

SMALL OCCUPATION

KNOWN AS

THE POTASH FARM

In the Parishes of Framsden and Ashfield

COMPRISING

An Old-fashioned Farmhouse, Double Cottage and Set of Agricultural Premises

in all embracing an area of

35 a.   2 r.   27 p.

of Deep Soil Arable and Pasture Lands

With Possession at Michaelmas Next

(Subject to the Cottage Tenancies)

WHICH

Woodward & Woodward

Are Instructed by MR. WIGHTMAN HOWARD,
to Sell by Auction, at the

Crown and Anchor Hotel, Ipswich

On TUESDAY, June 30th, 1936

At **3** o'clock in the afternoon, in 1 Lot.

MESSRS. TURNER MARTIN & SYMES,
4 & 6, ELM STREET, IPSWICH,
Vendor's Solicitors.

Newby, Printer, Stowmarket

End of London. He died at the age of thirty-one from injuries received in a pub fight. Apparently the rule in Canning Town was for police to enter public houses in pairs, but Horace, who from his photograph seems to have been a strong man, went in alone to stop a fight and was beaten up.

Sam died in 1921 and as a very small boy I was taken to visit his wife Elizabeth, my Great-grandmother, who was living in a cottage at Stowupland and being looked after by Great Aunt Kate. Before this, Kate had worked at a children's home in Needham Market, but her sister Emma, a plain, plump but rather jolly lady, worked as a housekeeper for an elderly farmer. Her employer, Wightman Howard, referred to as 'old Wightie' by the family, had Potash Farm at the north end of Framsden. Emma remained loyally with him for many years. The family went to enormous trouble, short of actually asking, to find out whether she also slept with him.

Every Sunday the family went to the Baptist chapel and the pastor would hammer home the message that sin was wicked and that anyone who was responsible for it must expect punishment. The punishment for sin was supposed to come in the next life, but had some of her family discovered that Emma had sinned she would have got quite a lot of punishment in this world as well. Emma was left out of her father's will and did not share in any of the £769 he left.

The land was good in Framsden and back in the 1860s there were twenty-eight independent farms in the villages. Some of these farms were little more than a small field with a tiny barn, but Old Wightie's 35 acres at Potash Farm was more typical. It divided up into eleven fields and 'pightles' (small meadows). Most of these enclosures were of only around 3 to 5 acres, about the size of a pony paddock, and the amount of hand work needed to keep those hedges cut back would have kept one man busy for most of the winter. Today, 35 acres would be just one field. Yet right up until the 1930s this small acreage provided a living for a farmer and his family and at least two men working for him.

The Howards appear to have bought Potash Farm when a large estate was broken up in the 1870s and Old Wightie inherited it from his father in about 1906. The surviving map shows that the land around the farm was all owned by the titled landowners. The Right Honourable Lord Henniker owned the land to the east, while the Countess of Dysart and the Earl of Gosford owned the fields to the west. These long-established landowners had little patches of land all over the country. There was no fixed pattern to land ownership, some estates lasted for generations in the same family, others only lasted one or two generations.

In 1936 Wightman Howard retired and moved with Emma to Stowmarket. His 35 acre Potash Farm, its farmhouse and two workers cottages were auctioned at the 'Crown and Anchor', Ipswich. In the sales particulars the farmhouse is described as 'old fashioned'. In fact the Charsfield children remember that to reach the farm one walked across a meadow and the drinking water was taken from the farm pond in a bucket, which resulted in 'polly wiggles' floating around in the tea. Whether there was any truth in the family's suspicions about Emma's relationship with Old Wightie, they were never resolved. It is said that she could have married him, but preferred to be housekeeper because then she had a weekly wage, which a wife probably would not have got. Chapel or no chapel, the country folk were very down-to-earth about financial matters.

Old Wightie left Emma the house in Stowmarket and her sister Kate went to live with her and later they lived in a little house in Bramford Lane, the down-market end of Ipswich. The two sisters lived lives based on thrift and never being in debt, nor asking for

8.Sitting in front Emma Simper, behind on the left is Margaret Simper and Kate Simper in about 1912.

help from anyone.Great Aunt Kate died in 1972 aged eighty-nine and was the last of her generation.

'Poor old Aunt Kate', everyone in the family used to say about this old lady, but she was not really poor. When she died everyone was amazed that she left £19,359, a considerable sum at that time for a lady living very modestly on the Bramford Lane. When the house was emptied it was discovered that pound notes were stored behind the wallpaper and under the linoleum on the bathroom floor. Obviously no-one was going to break into her house and steal the cash accumulated by decades of frugal living.

Herman Simper building a round corn stack at Brook Farm, Charsfield in about 1930.

Morris Turner of Boyton riding his horse, 1952.

Chapter Two

CHRISTMAS DINNER

CAN YOU TELL ME
IF ANY THERE BE
THAT WILL GIVE ME EMPLOYMENT
TO REAP AND SOW
TO PLOUGH AND MOW
TO BE A FARMER'S BOY
Popular nineteenth century song which became the countryman's anthem

In my quest to record how and why the countryside has changed, I have followed the course of my family back into the past. They were simply a typical family reacting to whatever economic and social changes hit the villages in eastern England. Revisiting over twenty farms they had been connected with, I find in nearly every case that the landscape must have greatly changed.

Records show that my grandfather Herman and Great Aunt Kate were born at Framsden, but their father, Sam Simper, left the Tollemache Estate and moved around a great deal. About 1900, he farmed on the edge of Ipswich at Sproughton and one of the Jacksons, who were at Sycamore Farm for several generations, remembered that when his family walked to church they would see Sam leading his family off to the nearest chapel. A family friend visited Herman when he was rolling barley on the land where the Ipswich Sugar Beet factory was later built. To save buying a roller, he had made one from a tree-trunk and had a horse pulling it.

In 1906 Sam was farming at Nelson Farm, Ashbocking. Of all the farms in East Suffolk which have some connection with the family, this is the only one which still has much the same appearance in 1999 as it did before 1914. It is still a family farm with small fields. Such agricultural units are becoming rarer every year. Once they come on to the market people from the towns buy the houses and buildings for homes, while the land is usually sold to link up with a larger holding.

In 1908 Sam was farming at Hill Farm, Clopton. This was a typical heavy land East Anglian holding of around 100 acres, a small neat brick farmhouse, big wooden barn and a few tiled outbuildings for cattle and horses. The farm buildings are at the top of a slight valley and during harvest the wagons used to go down empty, but when they came back, loaded with corn, a 'trace horse' (one horse in front of another) had to be put on to get them back up the hill.

I have no doubt that when Sam worked this land the farmstead would have been surrounded by small fields, each divided over the centuries into soil type and surrounded by a low neat hedge and a deep ditch for drainage. In 1998 the farmhouse appeared to be a private house, the buildings used by a straw merchant, and the land part of a larger holding.

In the Edwardian era the villages of heavy land Suffolk around Clopton were a maze of lanes dividing a mass of small farms with neat hedges. That must have been the scene

9. A horse-sail reaper of the type used on Street Farm, Framsden. Even with a sail reaper the corn still had to be tied by hand into shuffs. When a harvest was done with a sail reaper in heavy land Suffolk it took one man for every 12 acres of wheat.

when Margaret Rose and a friend went for a long walk in Clopton one summer's evening. As the girls walked along, they spotted a man in his late twenties hiding in the bottom of a ditch holding a shotgun. The girls stopped and asked him what he was doing down there.

The young man with the shotgun was Herman, my grandfather, a man with a great reputation for only spending money when absolutely necessary. He had heard the girls walking up the road and thought they were the local policeman. As he did not have a gun licence, he hid in the ditch. This was the beginning of the romance between Margaret Rose and Herman Simper which must have progressed well, because they were married in 1912. On his marriage certificate Herman is described as being 'a farmer of Hill Farm, Clopton'. From what I have been able to piece together from family memories, Sam, then quite an old man, had become ill and Herman was running the Clopton farm.

When Herman told Sam and Elizabeth that he was going to marry Margaret Rose, they were frankly horrified. How were they going to work the farm with Herman gone? Sam said, 'that girl can't even milk a cow, what good is she to you?'

'I showed them', Grandma Margaret used to recall, 'I went straight out and milked the nearest cow. They didn't say anything more after that!'

After the marriage had taken place, Herman and Margaret Simper 'set up' home at Brook Farm, Charsfield, where their seven children were born. Herman's enthusiasm for

10. Wedding of Herman Simper and Margaret Rose at White House Farm, Burgh, 1911. Kate stands behind Herman and Emma is to her left with young Hermy between them. Sam and Elizabeth Simper are on the couple's right and George and Mrs Rose on their left. Everyone in the wedding group is wearing a hat, the women's styles are wonderful. Herman continued to wear a bowler 'for best' for the rest of his life.

creeping around hedges shooting small animals and birds to eat stayed with him. When he was an old man, he had an incredibly ancient shotgun, with wire holding the barrel stock. There were passionate scenes in the Brook Farm kitchen as his wife and some of his daughters begged him, for his own safety, not to risk firing this terrible weapon at rabbits.

The village street at Charsfield is in a valley through which flows the brook which eventually becomes the River Deben. Brook Farm stands on its own on the south side of the brook. The farmhouse is a typical half-timbered Suffolk longhouse, probably built in the sixteenth century. The timber frames have long since been plastered over as successive generations have sought to up-date and improve the living conditions. During some forty-five years, when it was the home of Herman and Margaret Simper, it altered very little, except for indoor plumbing and electricity being installed.

The 95 acre Brook Farm was bought from the Duke of Hamilton in 1911 for £20 an acre, which was top price for land at that time. Grandfather Herman actually bought the farm in partnership with his older brother, Fred William, who had been running the 'Blue Posts' pub in Stowmarket. The partnership between the two brothers did not last long and Fred William went back to farming on his own. He moved to a farm at Harleston where he committed suicide. During the inter-war agricultural slump he was very worried about money and thought the banks were just about to close him down because an important cheque had not arrived. The morning after he killed himself the cheque arrived in the post.

When Herman and Fred William bought the farm, they did not know that the Duke of Hamilton had already gifted the top of Rookery Meadow to the Church of England to extend their graveyard. Grandfather Herman went off to Ipswich to see his solicitor, but the noble Duke pocketed the cash for the land given away and would not return it. Grandfather Herman had started to attend Charsfield Church, but after this land dispute, he switched his loyalty to the Baptist chapel at the other end of the village. He never forgot or forgave the Duke for the loss of 'his' land and insisted, slightly to his family's embarrassment, that he should be buried in the new churchyard. At least in the end he took possession permanently of a small part of the Rookery Meadow! That was not the end of the story, because it resurfaced again in Ronald Blythe's book *Akenfield*, much to Grandma Margaret's fury.

My grandmother Margaret's father, George Rose of White House Farm, Burgh, had given the newly-married couple £100 which paid for them to furnish the house and stock the farm for the first year. George Rose, who started as a tenant farmer and progressed to owning his own farm, used to 'walk a stallion'. He had a Suffolk stallion, which a man took around the district, walking up to twenty miles a day, 'covering' the mares. This must have been a profitable sideline and Rose thought such a lot of his stallion that he was kept in a shed in his garden.

In the opening years of farming on his 'own account' Herman was also a keen breeder of Suffolk horses. He kept six, two more than were needed to work the 90 acre farm, but he bred from two of the mares and sold the colts. In about 1919, in the boom just after World War I, a colt was sold for £110, an unheard of amount of money for a carthorse. Later Herman kept just four Suffolks to make up two plough teams.

The great advantage of these 'chesnut' Suffolk horses, the Suffolk farmers believed, was that as they did not have long hair on their legs they returned relatively clean from a day's ploughing in the wet heavy land. On the larger East Anglian farms the horseman's day began at 5am, when he arrived at the stables to feed, water, muck out and then harness up his horses. At 7am the men and horses left for the fields, the head horseman ALWAYS leading his horses out of the stable first. These horses were worked on the 'long shift', that is they stayed in the field for their eight hour working day and had a nosebag of 'bait' at midday.

On the smaller farms, where the stable was never very far away, the horses worked a 'short shift'. They returned to the stable at midday to eat their 'bait' there. On the heavy land, a man and a team of two horses were able to plough an acre a day, while on the light land they had to plough two acres a day. By that time, both man and beasts were exhausted and returned to the stables to rest for the night.

A horse was normally three years old before it started working and then it took about another two years to get it completely trained. Usually each man had sole use of a particular horse, and after two years a very close relationship developed and the horse would do anything the horseman quietly ordered.

In the early 1930s Brook Farm started to mechanise with a Fordson tractor. The first tractors were no faster than the horses, but they did not need to stop for 'bait' and could go on ploughing for hours on end. Also, horses had to be fed seven days a week, while a tractor would go in the shed on Saturday and need no further attention until Monday morning.

The other vital piece of mechanisation was the binder, which cut the corn and bound it up into 'shuffs' to be put into the wagons and carted to the farm and then stacked ready for threshing in winter. The binder at Brook Farm was temperamental to say the least. When in action Mr Blake, a blacksmith living several miles away, would cycle over with tools on his bike, 'set up' the binder and would run behind, making repairs to keep it going. Farmers and farm workers who had spent all their lives with horses and hand tools took some time to acquire the increasingly complicated skills needed to set up machines.

The largest field at Brook Farm was 24 acres, but Herman considered this far too big and divided it up into three pieces. Herman's management policy at Brook Farm followed the traditional pattern for heavy land East Anglia. Basically it was the four course system with a 'white straw' (wheat) year followed by beans and layers. Also, cattle were bought on Ipswich Market which spent the summer on low meadows near the house and then went in a yard to be fattened over winter. The muck from the yards was spread on the land to increase fertility. My father's only comment on Brook Farm was that Grandfather always bought more cattle than he had grass for. This influenced my father, who then spent his lifetime over-feeding his herd.

Some three years after Herman bought Brook Farm, Britain and Germany went to war and the subsequent food shortages shot prices up and helped to pay for the farm. In 1917, the German submarine campaign in the North Atlantic sank so many merchant ships coming in with food that Britain was being starved into collapse.

This created boom conditions in the grain market, with wheat rising to over 80 shillings a quarter (£19 a ton). After the war prices fell slightly and then suddenly halved in 1921. During the war costs had shot up and these did not go down to the pre-war level. Many farmers had bought their land from the great estates at war-time prices and faced great difficulties in the post-war period. Land prices, which had been around £45 per acre, also fell, ruining many farmers. From 1921 until the eve of World War II there was a long, hard period known to East Anglian farmers as the 'slump'.

One of the problems was that the millers preferred to use the hard Canadian wheat to the 'soft' varieties which grew in Britain. The Canadian wheat had an amazing journey from the prairies to the mills in the British ports. Wheat grown in Manitoba and Saskatchewan first went by railroad to the Great Lakes and then by steamer for several hundred miles, after which it was discharged into huge silos at ports on Lake Huron, followed by another long railroad trip across Ontario to Montreal, from where it was shipped down the St Lawrence to Europe. Some of this grain was shipped to the Royal Docks in London and then brought up the coast by sailing barges to Ipswich. After travelling about five thousand miles and being tranships at least eight times, wheat finally arrived at the Ipswich mills at a lower price than the farmers just outside the town could grow it for.

Since the eighteenth century, wheat had been the main arable crop in southern England. In the eyes of my grandfather and many men of his generation, land which would not grow wheat was not worth bothering with. Grandfather Herman was a good natured, rather thin man, with a drooping moustache. He was really an economic miracle because while many farmers all around him were going bankrupt, he kept steadily on. He worked continually, apart from going to Ipswich Market and chapel on Sundays, and did not have a real holiday until he was over seventy. On about 90 acres he brought up seven children, some of whom were sent to private school, and he was one of the first people in the village to purchase a car.

Herman's first car was a 25hp Ford in which he could get all his seven children. Then he had a Singer, which he turned over in a ditch on the way to Ipswich Market. After that he would not drive and my grandma positioned herself firmly behind the steering wheel.

He also bought several cottages in the villages, which only cost a few pounds each. One of these cottages was bought for Jack Petitt to live in. He worked for my grandfather all his life. The other worker on Brook Farm, Johnson, lived in a house he owned. The 90 acre farm needed three men to work it and later Herman's sons also had to help. Most of the work was done by hand, even fertiliser was hand spread by walking across the fields with buckets. By adding a little nitrogen they could on a good year get the wheat yields up from a ton an acre to just over a ton an acre.

One day in 1938, Herman walked across to his son Herman working in one of the fields and said, 'drive me into Ipswich, boy, I have just remembered I have made the final payment to the bank for the farm and I would like to go and collect the deeds.'

All this was achieved on quite a small amount of crops sold. As well as arable crops, eight cows were kept and milked in loose boxes near to the house. The milk was retailed over the half-door at the back of the farmhouse. Village people arrived with cans and the milk was ladled out in pints and half pints. A pint was sold for two pennies, while skimmed milk was sold to poorer families at one penny a pint. The skimmed milk was the result of butter-making, which took place once a week. This was made in a big churn which had to be turned by hand, a very hard job and one that the reluctant sons of the family were obliged to undertake. When the Milk Marketing Board was started, some of the milk was sold to them. Grandfather Herman was very much in favour of the Board because it gave a stable price and paid its bill monthly.

11. The Simper family at Brook Farm, Charsfield in about 1932. Front row left to right Philip, Herman, Margaret, Norman and Derek. Back left to right Herman, Joyce, Margaret and Betty

Another source of income came through having a small power mill installed in the big black wooden barn on the opposite side of the yard to the farmhouse. When the day's work was done Herman went out into the barn and ground corn into cattle food for his neighbours. In time, his four sons were pressed into helping on the farm, splashing through the mud to feed pigs in sties at the end of the barn and helping with manual work at harvest.

A few pieces of land were sold as building plots, the best sale being £25 for land for the Charsfield village hall around 1936. This was a useful sum, as Herman's annual income at the time was about £100 a year. Like most East Anglian farmers, Herman only survived the slump because of dairy cows and sugar beet. Seven acres of the new crop of sugar beet were grown and did not at this stage require expensive machinery, it was harvested by hand and then piled up beside the road to be forked on to a lorry.

In the inter-war years there were fifteen independent farms in Charsfield, mostly owner-occupied. Charsfield seems to have escaped the worst of the slump because a family from Kent, attracted by the cheap heavy land, had moved in and established apple orchards. The orchards generated a great deal of casual work during which the people worked hard and earned, for that period, high wages.

The women working in the orchards are reputed to have given generously to the Baptist chapel and kept it going. As a small boy in the 1940s I accompanied my parents to Charsfield Chapel's Anniversary. I have no idea what this was an anniversary of, but it was a major social event in the life of that village. The road outside the chapel was full of smartly dressed people walking along to attend, and the chapel was packed. My Grandparents proudly sat at the front of several pews which were filled with their children, their wives and girl-friends and at that time myself as the sole grandchild.

12. Herman Simper and Jack Pettit building a wheat stack at Brook Farm in about 1930.

Above: 13. The harvest on a family farm about 1932. Left to right Herman, Grandfather Herman, Derek and Norman. Near the wagon in the background is Jack Pettit, who spent most of his working life on Brook Farm.

Left: 14. Harvest at Brook Farm, Charsfield about 1947. Derek is on the binder holding Philip's son, Nigel, while Jack Pettit has moved over on the Fordson tractor to let Philip hold his daughter Jane on the driver's seat.

The singing was loud and cheerful and filled the tiny building, but the major attraction was Pastor Baker's sermon. He gave a spirited delivery, thumping the pulpit, with none of our clever quietly delivered Church of England stuff here. Sinners would be punished by the Lord's mighty hand. There was No Escape from Retribution. The country people loved to hear this. They thought they were exploited by their employers and the shopkeepers and greatly liked the idea that they would receive eternal punishment. In case this might be true, the farmers, shopkeepers and tradesmen in the congregation gave very generously to chapel funds.

At some point quite early in my life my parents dropped out of the annual visit to Charsfield Baptist Chapel's Anniversary. They and all my grandparent's children quietly defected, if they bothered about religion at all, to the Church of England. The annual gathering of the clan became Grandma Simper's Christmas Day dinner. A family which ate together, stayed together.

The cooking for the dinner, a midday meal, was always done by the women, presided over by my Grandma, who was always in command of the situation. The kitchen at Brook Farm always seemed to be full of steam and raised female voices, no man dared enter there, until after the meal was served. My Grandfather Herman appeared rather over-shadowed by all this activity, but in the afternoon he had his moment, when he solemnly presented each grandchild with a ten shilling note.

As my grandparents were leading members of the Baptist chapel, these early Christmas dinners were absolutely without alcohol. There was rumoured to be a bottle of whiskey in the house, kept for medicinal purposes, but Grandma Margaret made darn sure this was hidden where no-one would find it. One Christmas, my uncles and aunts could tolerate it no longer and staged a deputation, instigated by Albert, who only a few years before had been a Battle of Britain pilot, and found the lack of alcohol more than he could bear. Some of my uncles crept out of the back door and up the road to the Charsfield 'Horseshoes'.

The smuggling in of a surprisingly large amount of bottles livened up the evening no end. My grandparents took the hint and next Christmas there were some bottles of spirits and sherry on the side-board, although the consumption was carefully monitored.

Once, during tea at Brook Farm, my grandmother looked out of the window and said, 'there go the Boy Jack, feeding up!' Expecting to see a young man, I looked out, but instead there was their ancient farm worker in a flat cap and waistcoat carrying two buckets of meal out of the barn to the pigs. In the language of rural Suffolk, anyone younger than you was a Boy or Girl, regardless of age.

Grandfather Herman farmed until he was eighty and only gave up then because his bullocks got out, probably because they were hungry, and he and my grandma could not run fast enough to round them up, so they thought it was time to retire. My grandfather did not have a pension, as he had refused to pay a contribution, but my grandma did get one. Brook Farm was put on the market and sold for £70 an acre, an increase in just forty years of over three times the value, and they were delighted.

Brook House, just across the road, was purchased. This was an ideal place for their retirement, because from the living room window there was a good view of the 'T' junction at the end of Charsfield street. Even around 1958 there was limited traffic up Charsfield street and my grandparents could sit there and monitor everyone's movements. They worked out who was cycling to work late, who was going shopping in Ipswich and the occasional tractor movement between the farms would lead to a discussion on the progress of cultivation of the land around the village.

15. Herman Simper in his wagon at Brook Farm, Charsfield in 1949. They had just unloaded at the stack and were going back up the field for another load. Raymond Archer is on the horse and the Simpers riding in the wagon are Nigel, Betty, Herman, Marion and daughter Jane. Nigel was so impressed by these early visits to his grandfather's farm that he made a career in agriculture with Strutt and Parker.

In fact, they were very happy with village life and had little interest in the world at large. By then their seven children had all married, mostly into other farming families, and had produced seventeen grandchildren. As the Bible had told them, they had gone forth and multiplied.

For several years after my grandparents died the family rather drifted apart, but those great family gatherings were such a landmark in everyone's lives that Phillip Simper, the eldest son, instigated a Family Reunion. These in recent years have been held in Charsfield Village Hall, but although it is still possible to recognise the original seven, the ever-increasing circle of cousins and second cousins become harder to identify.

16. The ruined barn at Brook Farm, Charsfield in 1974. Every Suffolk farm had one or more barns and around this time hundreds were pulled down or fell down.

Chapter Three

TUESDAY MARKET

PEOPLE WILL ALWAYS NEED FOOD
W.F.Turner

As a child, Monday night was always bath night. This was the start of the preparation for going to Ipswich Market on Tuesday. The journey was one of the longest we undertook regularly during the war, and no doubt petrol coupons had to be saved in order to make it. We left the coastal villages, where apart from military vehicles there was very little traffic. When we reached the wild open heathland of Sutton Walks there was a possible pause. If the red flag was flying we had to wait until the planes undertaking mock bombing practice had gone over and then dash across the heath. Next, we crossed the bridge over the top of the River Deben to make a brief visit to the sleepy little country town of Woodbridge to collect groceries and accumulator batteries for the radio.

Then, the final leg of the twenty-two mile journey was completed to the county town of Ipswich. The town had one car park on the Tower Ramparts where about a hundred cars could be parked, although only on Tuesdays did it ever become full. From here my mother headed for the shops while with my father we undertook the long walk down to Ipswich Market. I never saw him buy any cattle, but we stood watching the store and fat cattle sold and then walked across the road to the cow and calf auction ring. We also walked around the pens of sheep and pigs that were for sale. Certainly progress around the Market was slow, partly because drovers, shouting and encouraging animals on with sticks, were constantly cutting a path through the groups of gossiping farmers and partly because every few yards we would meet another old friend and exchange a few words with him.

Most farmers spent all week on their farms and this was the only occasion they had to meet like-minded people. As a child I always thought my family had a lot friends in Ipswich, but when I became teenage I realised that they hardly knew anyone in the town. All the people we met at the Tuesday Market came in from the countryside.

The cattle dealers from the Midlands, who sometimes came down to Ipswich Livestock Market, liked stealing a deal with vigorous handshakes and the exchange of Luck Money, in which some of the purchase price was given back, but Suffolk people did not like any outward shows of emotion and certainly did not like parting with money.

On Tuesday afternoon the Corn Exchange was opened and we went there. This high Victorian building had the most extraordinary acoustics. The voices of the men on the floor echoed loudly under the glass roof high above with a noise which sounded like waves breaking on a beach. It must have been an architectural disaster, but in all the years we went there I never heard anyone comment on this weird effect.

In the Corn Exchange real business was clearly undertaken. Each firm had a little wooden rostrum with its name on the front and one or two men standing behind. By the 1940s the use of the telephone was just beginning to replace this weekly visit to the merchants, but all corn trading used to take place here.

Each farmer produced a sample of the corn which he had to sell in a little bag. The merchant would tip some grain into his hand for inspection and hold it up to the light.

17. Jack Bater, Pearl's uncle, in the Devon Yeomanry about 1905. Jack and Harry Bater went to Canada, but after farming there for several years their barn burned down and they returned to Devon. They could not adjust to farming the small fields, or to the lack of machinery, so they moved to East Anglia. They finished farming at Bucklesham Hall, Suffolk. The Baters were on friendly terms with the Turners because both families were amongst the small number of West Country farmers who came up country to take over Suffolk arable farms.

18. Ipswich Cornhill, the old market place, in 1824. In 1868 the medieval Moot Hall on the right was replaced with a Victorian Town Hall. Behind this, the new Corn Exchange replaced the market cross in 1882.

At once, the haggling began: 'Oh dear what a pity Master, could have been a good sample. Well it might even have made malting. You can see it's a little on the thin side and just a little bit too pale', the merchant would say, shaking his head like a doctor breaking very bad news to a patient.

'That!' the farmer would reply angrily, 'must be the best sample of malting barley you have seen this year!'

'Look, before the war', the merchant would say, now trying the honest friend giving good advice technique, 'when the malsters only bought in these eastern counties that sample might have made top price, but you know the malsters are now buying barley in Yorkshire!'

Then a price was agreed, and the deal sealed in quiet Suffolk fashion with a slight nod or twist of the head.

Even during the war, when prices and profits must have been high, I never heard anything but gloom on Ipswich Market. Things were always getting worse. After the war the real gloom started.

'You will see', farmer after farmer agreed, 'it will be just like the last lot (referring to World War I), once the boom is over farming will collapse, they dropped us pretty quickly last time and they'll do it again, you will see.'

The Labour Party, which swept to victory just after World War II, had no sympathy for farmers. In the new Britain they thought they were creating, all major industries were to be nationalised and placed under state control. Still, Rome was not built in a day and the

19. Ipswich Cornhill with trolley buses in about 1910. Although Ipswich had grown away from being just a market town its industries, milling, fertiliser and machinery manufacture were still based on agriculture.

Government of Clement Attlee knew that it would not stay in power if rationing was not ended quickly and the shops filled with food. After the cost of World War II, Britain was effectively bankrupt and had to grow its own food, not resume the old policy of buying as much as possible from abroad.

The policies and laws brought in just after World War II changed the countryside over the next thirty years. The message was clear, produce all the food you can and don't worry about the cost because we will subsidise it. To achieve this, the Government brought in extra payments on just about everything, from removing hedgerows to a headage payment on livestock.

Most of the farming community of east Suffolk attended Ipswich Market and divided up into huge loose-knit clans. The tenants from the big estates tended to meet in the same place and well out of the range of agents' ears to discuss local affairs, but mostly it would be the huge family groups who met up. We always went for lunch at the Waterloo with my grandparents Turner, Morris and Nell. The Turners were a very different family to the Charsfield side. Although nominally Church of England, their passions were business and riding horses.

Morris Turner was a tall, upright man with a crisp little moustache and always had the bearing of an officer and a gentleman. He had been a captain in the British Army during World War I, which had led him to be invited as a magistrate on the Woodbridge bench in about 1943. He always claimed that when he first turned up at the Shire Hall, Woodbridge he felt a little intimidated because he was the only magistrate without some form of title. Morris seems to have been very fair as a magistrate, but he was a man with strong views and had a short fuse. He often lost his temper with the men who worked on his farm. These little confrontations must have blown over very quickly, because the same men stayed with him for years.

Before 1939, most farm workers were hired on a daily basis. When it was wet the farmer could send them home and not pay them.

Our old horseman at Manor Farm used to say, 'We were stood up against a wall like a gang of harrows in the winter and got noth'en.'

Grandfather Turner would never send his men home, saying that the poor devils earnt little enough to feed their families even if they worked all week.

Sometimes on the way home from Ipswich Market we called on Morris' father, William Frederick Turner, who had retired to Foxhall Road where he had a tiny bungalow named Berghersh, after one of his farms. My great-grandfather W.F. Turner, known as Will to his relations, was a busy little man, who hated being retired. He had many extraordinary tales to tell about his business life. My grandmother Nell Turner did not really approve of all her father-in-law's wheeling and dealing, but they intrigued me.

Will Turner had grown up on a small grazing farm in Nottinghamshire, but his family saw no future in farming and said he must go to London and make his fortune. In about 1880 Will left home to walk to the station to catch a train for London. His mother had given him boiled eggs to eat on the journey. Will got bored, and to liven things up he threw the boiled eggs at posts as he passed. In his years as an apprentice tailor in the East End of London he often thought of those fresh farm eggs and how much he would have enjoyed them.

In time, he set up his own tailor's shop, mostly employing Jews who had escaped the persecution in Russia. It made a living, but not the fortune he always craved. He became a bookmaker and went around to the race tracks with my great-grandmother as his clerk.

Eventually Will Turner had trouble with the gangs demanding protection money on the race tracks and he decided to leave the East End of London.

He bought the 'George and Pilgrims', then the main hotel in the centre of Glastonbury on the Somerset plains. He was reputed to have been one of the wealthiest men in the little West Country town and it was a great talking point that when his daughter Ethel went for her music lessons, a carriage drawn by a pair of horses drew up at the front door.

Morris had been trained as a tailor and could make his own clothes, but he hated this. Morris wanted to go into farming so Will sold the 'George and Pilgrims' and bought farms at Over Stowey and Adscombe. The two men were to remain great friends and often business partners.

Morris married Nell Champion, whose mother had small shops in Glastonbury, and they went to live at Manor Farm, Over Stowey. Two of their four children were born on this farm and all was going well until World War I broke out. Morris had been a keen member of the Somerset Yeomany and the Government had paid him to keep a riding horse, so he was 'called to arms'.

When Morris received his call to arms, he rode off to war on his horse in uniform with his rifle and joined his unit in the centre of Bridgwater. They were prepared and trained to fight a dashing war of cavalry charges, but grandfather used to laugh and say, 'we soon left the horse behind.'

He was shipped off to Egypt to fight the Turks in Palestine, but seems to have spent most of his time driving a Ford truck in the desert. Twenty-five years later I found his rusty old cavalry sword down in the cellar at Valley Farm, Boyton. My grandmother Nell had banned his weapon from the living room.

'Did you kill anyone in that war?' I asked, a small boy full of blood lust. My mother and grandmother looked rather worried about this enquiry, but my tactful grandfather replied 'Boy they all ran away so fast I never got near enough to kill anyone.'

I am not sure now that this was the truth, because he took part in the heavy fighting in the disastrous Gallipoli campaign in 1915. This was one of Churchill's bright ideas and was intended to stop the Dardenelles entrance of the Black Sea falling into German hands. Poor maps and tactical blunders by the generals resulted in the troops being landed without any clear idea of what the terrain or fortifications ahead were like. In fact, the Somersets and the Anzacs regiments found themselves pinned down on the beaches by Turkish soldiers in fortified positions in the craggy heights above them. In the ten months before the peninsula was evacuated there was heavy loss of life amongst Allied troops.

Grandfather was wounded and remembered being carried to a field hospital and hearing other soldiers talking about a man expected to die in the night. Then he realised they were talking about him, but he did survive both that night and the war and returned in time to his Somerset farm.

During the war, Britain had come dangerously near to starvation, due to the success of the German submarine campaign in 1917, and political leaders had promised that if farmers made a tremendous effort to produce food they would not be forgotten. After the war, in the brave new world, the men who had been fighting did not expect the countryside to be allowed to slip back into the rural slum it had been throughout much of the Victorian period. However, events overtook everyone. In 1921 the price of wheat effectively halved, going from 80 shillings a quarter down to 42 shillings a quarter. Reading back through newspapers of 1921 the leader writers and the general public were all furious with farmers for asking for help. It was their own fault, served them right if they could not sell their

20. A competition in 1910 'chopping out' (singling) sugar beet with hand hoes.

21. It was not just farms that used a lot of hand labour. Here Percy Bumstead is hand 'ploughing' barley for malt at the Fox Maltings, Needham Market, 1971. This was one of the last of the old floor maltings to operate in East Anglia.

wheat. They had grown the wrong variety of wheat, what was all this rubbish about low prices?

Will Turner tried to think of a solution to the problem. He read that land in East Anglia was half the price of land in Somerset. It seemed a good idea to move to this place called Suffolk and buy twice as much land as they had in Somerset and then perhaps he would make a living again. The farms at Over Stowey and Adscombe were sold, for a high price, and in no time the Turners were loading their belongings into lorries and heading east.

Will bought Home Farm, Capel St Andrew, a large light land farm near the coast, and was very proud of it as one of his fields was 100 acres (it has since been divided up into several small units). Morris bought a small heavy land farm in the centre of the county opposite the maltings at Earl Stonham. The move east didn't turn out to be entirely successful because the agricultural slump just got steadily worse.

In Somerset the Turners had been doing 'dog and stick' grassland farming. Very little labour was involved and not much capital was needed because the livestock reproduced themselves and whatever could be sold made a little profit. The Suffolk cereal farms were totally different, they needed a small army of men and women labouring away in the fields to produce a crop. Wages in the inter-war years were still very low, but the price of wheat was even lower.

Morris had found that the Earl Stonham farm did not pay, so he bought three lorries, kept in a wooden shed beside the road, and got the contract to haul malt from Stonham Maltings just across the main road. Those lorries appear to have been 3-tonners and were started with a crank handle. On one cold morning when a lorry would not start Morris put his back out hand-cranking it and suffered with this for the rest of his life.

Morris did not stay at this farm in heavy land Suffolk for very long and after a few years he moved to the Sandlings peninsula where he bought Valley Farm, Boyton from an estate which had gone bankrupt. Boyton was a light land village between the sea and the heathland and was then made up of small farms. In the summer the farmers and their families met every Sunday and played tennis, but by the mid-1930s Morris was the only one of this group who had not gone bankrupt. Morris said he owed the bank so much money that he lay awake all night worrying that when he went in to draw cash for his men's wages the bank manager would see him, call him in and ask for the growing overdraft to be repaid.

Valley Farm joined up with Will Turner's farm. The agent responsible for winding-up the bankrupt estate asked Will to take on Abbey and Ferry Farms, Butley. He was given an extra thousand acres to farm rent-free, just to keep it in cultivation. He also had the grazing marshes around the Butley River and particularly liked the Barrow Hill, claiming the cattle could move around it and always stand in a sheltered place and so fatten quickly.

After two years however, the agent came and said: 'Mr Turner, you must buy this land off us, you can have it for £4 an acre.'

Will, always a man ready to drive a hard bargain, would have nothing of it because, in those two years with wheat under £5 a ton he had only been able to break even with the Butley land. He explained 'look, I can buy good wheat land, all I want for £4 an acre, I don't want this sandy rubbish for that sort of money.'

Not long afterwards the Greenwells, who had sold an estate just outside London for housing, gave about £20 an acre for the Butley land. Will thought this was too good to be true and promptly sold them his Home Farm and moved inland to buy Berghersh Place, Witnesham. All this gave him a great deal of worry and his doctor advised him to visit Switzerland. He was the first member of my family to have taken a holiday abroad.

22. The Great London March in 1939. Victor Shepherd of Shottisham Hall is in the centre carrying a shuff of corn on a pitchfork.

Wheat reached an all-time low in 1934, when it was sold for 20 shillings a quarter, about £4 a ton. After over ten years of the rural community being completely abandoned, the Government finally got around to thinking they had to do something about it. A vast amount of arable land had gone out of cultivation and the brighter politicians, who guessed there was another war coming with Germany,knew they had to get food production going again. First, they tried paying a small subsidy on the oats grown, which helped, then the introduction of free school milk improved things even more and eventually, in 1937, the first subsidy on wheat was paid. After this, every harvest was a little better than the one before.

In the 1920s, Will Turner went to Ipswich Market in a pony and trap. His favourite pastime was to go to the 'Crown and Anchor' Hotel where, in a large room on the second floor, farms which the banks had seized were put up for auction. They had to be sold and Will began buying farms very cheaply, sometimes with an opening bid. As he did not know Suffolk very well, he often had farms knocked down to him in villages he had never heard of. Afterwards he joyfully met Morris and Nell for tea, waving the sales particulars of some property he had just bought.

'Here Morris, run me out in your car tomorrow and see if we can find this place I just bought'. Grandmother Nell Turner was not amused that in those very hard times some useless derelict farm in the middle of nowhere had been purchased with money that the family did not have. Will was always optimistic, knowing that people would always need food. Sometimes he farmed the land himself, but he was very keen on finding 'likely' young men and putting them in the farms as working foremen. If the man proved he could manage the land, Will arranged for a bank to lend him the money to buy the farm. In this way, farms knocked down for a few pounds an acre could be resold for twice the money.

In Victorian times a system of weekly carriers carts had grown up linking most villages to the towns. The first cars were usually bought by the grand landowners or by doctors, but by the late 1920s farmers were buying them. Will Turner bought his first car when he was in his fifties, but never really mastered the art of controlling it. His second wife Nellie did not help by not telling him, when he was driving the wrong way up a one-way street in Norwich, she said that the people shaking their fists at him were just bad-mannered!

Although in the inter-war years many farmers bought their first primitive tractors, most of the time they were desperately short of money and their workers badly under-paid. Early in 1939 the East Anglian farmers and workers, spurred on by the success of the miners' protest march through London, decided to have their own march.

By that time, agriculture had been in recession for nearly twenty years and the farmers thought perhaps it was time for the Government of the day to come up with a policy to give the country population a decent livelihood. The Great London March of February 1939 was the result of this long frustration, but was finally organised because farmers said they had no faith in the Minister of Agriculture.

A special train was hired to take some 600 Suffolk farming folk from Ipswich to Liverpool Street station. All the farmers joined up to march to Westminster behind a band playing the 'Farmer's Boy' and with banners proclaiming 'Justice for the Land'. The photographs of the protesters at Westminster Central Hall show our little family group, my parents, Father's brother Herman and grandfather Morris Turner and his son Joe Turner. I was still only three and was left at home, and I think my parents really rather enjoyed the excitement of that rare visit to London.

However, the Government was at pains to take the steam out of this march and replaced the Minister of Agriculture the night before, so the Great March had to become a victory, not a protest event. In fact, events overtook the farming protest movement because Hilter's insane ambitions launched Europe into another major world war, bringing its chronic food shortages.

I last met my great-grandfather Will Turner on a summer evening in about 1946, when he came over to visit our Bawdsey farm. He wanted me to walk around the farm with him, but I stayed indoors listening to my favourite radio programme, 'Much Binding in the Marsh'.

By the time he died in 1948, Will had recouped the fortune he had lost in the farming slump of the inter-war years. From his tiny Ipswich bungalow he managed a mini-land empire and left eight farms. Morris and his sister Ethel Diamond, neither of whom were particularly bothered about great wealth, sat in their solicitor's office in Ipswich and tossed a coin to see who would have each property.

My grandparents used to talk a lot about Will's career, but I had no idea where any of his farms were. Morris, a well respected JP and farmer, was not interested in all the endless problems of land ownership and management. Besides, my grandmother Nell kept saying, 'remember what happened last time Morris, the politicians promised they would look after farming and then ruined us, for goodness sake sell those farms before they become worthless again.'

Exactly the opposite happened. The farms were sold, but the price of land kept climbing up steadily, not because money could be earned out of farming, but because since World War II farmland has always been sold at a premium.

23. Some of the Suffolk womenfolk at the Great London March, 1939. Joyce Jarold, Mrs M.C. Cooper, Janet Cooper and Julie Goodwin.

Chapter Four

FADED PARADISE

GOD SPEED THE PLOUGH
On the back of a settee in the Levington 'Ship'

My parents, Norman Simper and Lilian Turner, were married in 1936 at Boyton. My father wanted to go into farming and there were plenty of farms to choose from. The whole of Suffolk was a patchwork of little holdings, mostly belonging to the large estates, and the majority of landlords were desperate for tenants to keep their land in cultivation and provide them with some income. The limiting factor was the amount of capital available and in this case there was virtually none, just the few pounds saved from keeping pigs in rented barns, but my grandfather Herman put in a good word at the bank and this was enough to cover my father until the first harvest.

Father was very keen to build up a dairy herd, so he chose to rent the 170 acre Fir Tree Farm, Blaxhall from the Viscount Ullswater because it had grass marshes. There were three of them working this, which was really under-manned, but they were all young men and Father particularly worked very hard and ploughed on determinedly through any dif-

24. Norman Simper with a Suffolk horse at Fir Tree Farm, Blaxhall 1938.

ficulties. One man was the cowman, who hand-milked the twenty-four cows, Father going out after tea and pumping up water by hand for yards full of cattle. Although the herd was a jumble of breeds, the bull was a shorthorn, a breed then popular because it was 'dual-purpose', being beef cattle which milked quite well.

Four Suffolk horses were needed to work the farm, but after two years a Fordson tractor on iron wheels was purchased. This had to have iron hoops put on the wheels when it went on the road and the vibration, even on the fields, was back-breaking. 'Terrible thing' father snorts when remembering his first tractor.

Viscount Ullswater had been Speaker in the House of Commons and was concerned that his estate should look very attractive when he was driven around it. The problems of making a farm earn a living for its tenant were not uppermost in his mind.

The Ullswater estate was a very ancient block of land which between 1648-1833 had belonged to the Sheppard family. The centre of the estate was Ashe High House, a vast Elizabethan-style mansion, which was pulled down in 1949 when the estate broke up and the land was sold off. As a boy, when staying with my cousin Richard Turner at Ash Green Farm, we used to climb over the garden wall and play in the abandoned and badly overgrown gardens of Ashe High House. There was a huge garden chair-back which looked like the stern galley of a wooden warship. I seem to remember being told that this had

25. Frank Ling with Suffolk horses Boxer and Prince at a ploughing match at Blaxhall in 1938.

come from one of the ships that had sunk at the Battle of Sole Bay in 1672. Now at a more sceptical age I look back and think it was probably a piece of Edwardian romanticism.

Frank Ling, who was horseman at Fir Tree Farm, used to say he could remember me as a small boy coming into the stable and walking right under the Suffolk horses, but this is a complete blank to me. I do remember playing in the stackyard with some other children and falling from the back of a wagon. Also, I recall my mother holding me up at a bedroom window to look at a heron feeding in the pond down the lane behind the house. We left that farm when I was three, yet when I went back into the house over fifty years later I remembered the layout exactly. It was a very strange feeling, as if I had been there in another life.

There was no room at Fir Tree Farm to expand the dairy herd and one morning when father was helping to load the milk churns on to the lorry the driver told him that Mr Forrest, the Scotsman farming Manor Farm, Bawdsey, had died. He had collapsed of a heart attack on Ipswich Market. Father contacted the agent, Mr Walker, and got the farm.

In 1940 we left Blaxhall and moved to the larger Manor Farm, Bawdsey. Fir Tree Farm had been on rather poor light land and the rent was 12 shillings (60p) an acre per year while Manor Farm, a much better holding, was almost double the rent at £1 an acre. A big step up and plenty of grass for the dairy herd.

Manor Farm was then part of the Bawdsey Estate and most of the farms on this estate were around 250 acres, but in the slump of the 1930s the Estate had been putting the farms together to try and make economic units. Manor Farm, with another farm, Peyton Hall, Ramsholt, was a combined holding of 500 acres. Although father had one Fordson tractor for ploughing, it was several years before he could afford another one. So five horses were needed for cultivation and 'carting about' on Manor Farm and four horses on Peyton Hall.

Manor Farm stands alone on the top of a slight hill, blasted from the south-west by wind coming across the marshes and from the east by biting cold winds coming in from the

26. Farm horses resting at a ploughing match. At a ploughing match the prizes were for ploughing the land while at a drawing match they were just for ploughing a straight furrow.

North Sea. The farmhouses and buildings date from the various periods of agricultural prosperity. The oldest part of the house, a timber-framed Suffolk long house, date from around 1575 with another front part added a couple of decades later. It was built during the Elizabethan period when there was a great hunger for land. The wooden stable and flint granary, cobbled together with material from older buildings, date from inflated wheat prices during the Napoleonic Wars.

The golden years before the repeal of the Corn Laws were represented by a thatched brick riding stable, built for an influential farmer called Samuel Gross. On the other hand the main barn and cattle buildings date from the late Victorian period when farming was doing very badly. However, the farm had been bought by the highly successful London stockbroker, William Quilter, who spent a fortune developing his new Bawdsey Estate to try and re-generate this depressed area.

Through his dealings in the City of London, Sir William Cuthbert Quilter was by 1880 able to buy land at Bawdsey, overlooking the mouth of the River Deben, where he built a country villa, Bawdsey Manor, for summer visits. As his wealth rapidly increased Quilter extended his villa, until it became a rather disjointed country house, the central feature of his new Bawdsey Estate.

The Sandlings peninsula had been a patchwork of tiny estates and most of this land Quilter eagerly gobbled up to create the Bawdsey Estate. All the former landowners, the Tollemaches, Sheppards, the Wallers and most of all Lord Rendlesham, were very happy to sell, because in the long agricultural depression of the late Victorian period farm rents had been very low. By the early 1900s Quilter's agent was travelling up to the Houses of Parliament to negotiate the purchase of tracts of land, much of it open heathland, from Lord Rendlesham.

With the acquisition of all this land, Quilter became all powerful in the area. The public road to Bawdsey Ferry had run right past his new house, so Quilter had it re-routed and

27. A 'threshing tackle' at 'Farming in the Past' at Wantisden Hall. 1998. The forks are stuck in the colder at the side of a Ransome's drum.

laid a new road on faggots across the marshes out of his way. He is also credited with making sure the old track across the Sutton heath was abandoned in favour of a road running to the west next to land he had bought.

The Quilter family did not spend a great deal of time at Bawdsey Manor. Mostly they lived in London, spent the summer on various yachts, then in the autumn came down to Bawdsey for the pheasant shooting season. Then they would go to the south of France for the late part of the winter. They did not go to the Mediterranean in the summer because they had no desire to acquire brown skin like field workers.

Quilter was given a baronetcy, reputedly having refused to accept a mere knighthood 'several times', and became a Member of Parliament. His chief cause was to try and introduce a bill for pure beer. This made him very popular with the working men of Britain, but not everyone in East Suffolk welcomed the arrival of the rich young man from London. While most men were happy to touch their cap to the new land magnate, the Vicar of Bawdsey, an ancient Irishman called Allott Tighe-Gregory, totally ignored him. Sir Cuthbert Quilter was furious and tried to get him dismissed for not carrying out the duty of a clergyman properly.

One Sunday, Quilter took a party of family and his friends up the river by yacht to Ramsholt, where Tighe-Gregory also held the living. They arrived at the church to find Tighe-Gregory, who was over ninety and the oldest clergyman in the Church of England, locking the door. Quilter stormed up to him and demanded a service, but Tighe-Gregory just told him to be on time next week and got on his three-wheeled cycle and pedalled slowly back to Bawdsey.

Quilter fought back and built a chapel of corrugated iron within the grounds of Bawdsey Manor and ordered all his tenants, who comprised the whole village, to attend church there. But a Church of England vicar could not be dismissed and Tighe-Greogory stayed until he died.

Another man who had not seen eye to eye with the new big-wig from London was Samuel Chilton Gross, who had been tenant of our Manor Farm. He had taken the tenancy of the farm in about 1850 and by the time Quilter arrived Gross was Overseer of the Poor and a leading figure in the parish. Quilter wanted to create the best pheasant shooting in the eastern counties and he ordered Gross to have his hounds destroyed. The legend at Manor Farm was that after Gross' beloved hounds were destroyed he killed himself. Some of the old men claimed to have seen the blood on the floor.

Even when Quilter's Bawdsey Estate had been going for around twenty years people were still writing (anonymously) to the local papers complaining that the new breed of gamekeeper was shooting all the cats and dogs on the Estate. Looking back, Quilter's total disregard for the freedom of choice for working people makes him sound like a tyrant, but he was actually very popular during his day. In fact he appears to have been a rather down-to-earth man who had a shrewd knowledge of how to control the majority by pleasing them.

His wife, Lady Quilter, was very keen on 'good works' and in the summer there were often camps in the Manor grounds for young people from the poorer districts of the big cities. The Quilters had hit the jackpot in life and did not mind sharing it. They said that every man living on the Estate would have a job and a good cottage. No-one had ever promised that before.

To achieve this, Quilter had an estate yard and office built in Bawdsey and from there workers went out repairing the houses, building new ones and improving all the farm

28. Harry Ferguson on the left watches one of his new left hand auto-control ploughs being tested in the 1930s.

29. Pearl's father Harry Bater on a tractor pulling a binder on Bucklesham Hall about 1938.

buildings on the estate. Bawdsey became a Model Village at the centre of this mini-welfare state. Good craftsmen from all over the county were recruited and by the time we moved there, very few old local working families were left.

The families of working men who had been in the district for generations gravitated down to Alderton, the neighbouring village, where the plain red brick rows of cottages were mostly pre-Quilter. The two villages hated each other, the estate office clerks and craftsmen of Bawdsey looked down on the labourers of Alderton, while the tough pub fighters of Alderton thought the new Bawdsey people were a soft lot of boss's pets.

The generosity of the Quilter's Bawdsey Estate worked well so long as the 'right old' Quilter was alive and making money to support it, but after he died in 1911 the fortune he had created slowly dried up. His son Sir Cuthbert Ely Quilter was a kind man who enjoyed his pheasant shooting. Wherever he went on his estate people rushed forward to tell him everything was marvellous and he believed them.

When we arrived, the Estate was being run by the agent, George Walker, a likeable man from the Scottish Borders who tried to please everyone, but knew he was the captain of a sinking ship. The agricultural slump of the inter-war years had hit this estate very hard. The tenants of the worst farms walked out and the estate took them 'in hand' and farmed them at a loss to give employment. There were probably at least five hundred cottages on the estate and the rent of most of these was very low, while many estate workers paid no rent at all. Yet the annual repair bill for all these houses, when it was carried out, must have been astronomical.

To make things worse, the North Sea decided to eat away one side of the estate. The Bawdsey Estate created a Beach Gang to work on the foreshore repairing groynes, but to try and solve the problems Dutch engineers were brought in and built massive sea defences at East Lane. Actually this defence lasted until the great north-east gale of 1996 and saved the village of Bawdsey. Had the sea been able to get in on the marshes behind there would have been little to stop it washing away the whole village. However, nearly fifty years before this the Quilters had sold up here and most of the newcomers moving in had never even heard of them, let alone been grateful for their crippling expense.

Although people were always talking about Sir Cuthbert Ely, I never really met him. The nearest I got to him was when riding back from the Glebe Field one day, sitting on the back of the comfortable Suffolk horse gripping the wooden seals, when the horseman, Walter Halls, jerked the bridle of the horse to stop it and said, 'woo back old gal, here come old Quilter.'

Moving slowly up the lane to the farm, dodging the pot-holes, was a rather old car driven by a chauffeur. I just caught a glimpse of an elderly figure in the back seat. What struck me was that this car, conveying the great land-owner around his vast estate, which must originally have been rather grand, was then quite shabby.

The explanation for this came in 1999 in a visit from eighty-six year old Tony Barnard who had been Quilter's farm manager before 1950 on their Bawdsey, Sutton and Ramsholt Lodge farms. He recalled that he had been obliged to employ every man in the villages who wanted a job, but this labour force was highly inflexible. The seven gamekeepers would never lift a sack while forestry men, refused to work on the farms.

As sprays were never used a vast army of men was sent out hand harrowing weeds. This method of farming on light land before irrigation, produced yields of only half a ton an acre of barley and on a good year just 7 tons of sugar beet an acre. Even during the boom years of World War II, this method always lost money.

Chapter Five

THE WAR BETWEEN BAWDSEY AND GERMANY

INCREASE YOUR YIELDS
IN ALL YOUR FIELDS
Government wartime slogan

The Second World War was very personal, 'they' were dropping bombs on us and 'we' were going to give them a damn good hiding. When we moved to Bawdsey in 1940 there was not much sign of the war, but this quickly changed. The beaches were mined to prevent a German invasion and the whole coastal district became one massive military zone. There were army camps and anti-aircraft and searchlight units all along the coast. When we went to visit my grandparents in Boyton at night we passed several camps with armed sentries standing at the gates.

There was considerable military activity on our farm. There had been a searchlight unit on the hilltop before we arrived, but they had been shipped off and then taken prisoner in the fall of Singapore. Another searchlight unit arrived one day and I remember the thrill of riding in their lorry down to the grass on the marshes. I think they must have been trying to pick out planes attempting to bomb the RAF radar base at Bawdsey Manor.

Just before the war the Government had purchased Bawdsey Manor and about 120 acres so that Sir Watson-Watt and a small team of enthusiastic young scientists could develop what became radar. The team, based in the Manor stables and using very primitive equipment, managed to progress radar far enough by the time World War II started that it made a major contribution to winning the Battle of Britain. With the aid of radar the RAF could be told when German planes were coming in across the North Sea and send up planes to intercept them. This allowed a very few aircraft to be used accurately, thereby saving RAF time in going up to intercept what could have been allied aircraft.

My father was in the Observer Corp which identified aircraft coming in from the North Sea. They had ISS which could identify whether the planes were allied or enemy, but they had to visually recognise each enemy type. The real problem was enemy aircraft 'hedge hopping' below 2000 feet to get under the radar, making it impossible to get an ISS fix. Three people were needed to man the ISS equipment. The regular daytime Observer Corp manned the tower in Alderton during the day and Father, another farmer and the local butcher were 'volunteers' doing a night-shift. This meant that after spending all night watching out for aircraft, father often cycled home at 5.30 am to start milking the cows.

Nazi Germany seriously under-rated just how vitally useful radar was. Certainly it was not difficult to spot the four 247ft high radar towers sitting beside the sea in the Bawdsey Manor grounds. I think the Germans only seriously attempted to bomb the towers once, but on one occasion they dropped tons of silver paper which was intended to disrupt the radar. I can't tell you how thrilling it was to go out into the fields and find silver paper everywhere.

The war in the air resulted in the arrival of an anti-aircraft gun unit which dug in around the farm. There were two anti-aircraft gun pits in the garden and another two beside the farm road and an underground headquarters in a pit beside the farm buildings. The idea was that they were going to shoot down planes coming over Hollesley. The officer cheerfully said that when they opened fire it would break every window in our farmhouse.

Fortunately, the angle was wrong so they never fired a shot and one day I came home from school to find the gun pits empty. The whole abandoned camp made a wonderful area to play in. There was also a great sense of relief when the army pulled out because the relationship with them had been very strained. The young soldiers were expert egg thieves and in their desperate attempt to keep warm during the winter they had burnt every piece of wood they could find.

It might have been the presence of the abandoned gun pit surrounding the farm which lead to the dramatic attack. One summer evening I was almost asleep in my bedroom at the front of the farmhouse when I heard the roar of planes flying very low. Jumping out of bed, I saw three German planes flying straight towards the houses and little spurts of dust in the field showed where machine gun bullets were hitting the ground. I ran like mad into my parents' bedroom at the back of house and my mother and I hid under the bedclothes as the bullets hit the tiles and the front of the house.

My father had been cycling home, that fine summer evening, from a cricket club meeting when he heard the aircraft coming and had to jump off his bike and run for shelter behind the little cottage near the farm. The next day most of the village came up to look at the damage and the bullets were gathered up and left on the lawn for weeks. The sideboard with bullet holes still stands at the top of the stairs at Manor Farmhouse, but this incident left a much deeper mark on me. Until I was middle-aged if I heard a prop plane at night I would lie in bed and be tense with fear.

The shafting of the farm by the Luftwaffe had a silver lining. Our herd of cows, a mixed bunch of mostly Shorthorns, was happily grazing in Backhouse meadow behind the farm. Some of these unfortunate animals were hit and full compensation was paid by the government. Some cows did die, but others recovered, much to my father's delight. The compensation helped towards buying another much needed tractor.

At the beginning of the war, planes flew over to bomb the big cities, but at the very end the German pilots often just came in over the coast and let go their bombs. Once during Sunday lunch we heard a German plane and then a tremendous explosion as a bomb went off on our Butchers Hill field. It took a gang of land girls with a tractor days to fill up the hole.

The talk and gossip were nearly always about the war. Once a bomb landed near our school, damaging the school-house, and we all had a day off. I really quite enjoyed the war, everyone was very friendly and there were exciting things happening all the time. Once, a German plane crashed beside the pond down East Lane. We all went there to watch the soldiers clearing up the wreckage. Playing on the edge one boy found a 'hair bush', but it turned out to be a German's scalp and we all rushed off.

I first went to school in the Bawdsey village school. There was a mixed class, but I have not much recollection of the girls. The school had two playgrounds, for boys and girls, and a very high brick wall between them. Sometimes when the coke heap on the boys' side was high we climbed up on it and lobbed down bits of coke at the girls who were playing on the other side. This usually lead to one of the girls going screaming for the teacher. When the coke was low, bits were lobbed over blind, but I think the idea was to hit the girls' privy door when it was occupied. Small boys in rural Suffolk in the 1940s were not very refined.

Nearly all the children's parents had some connection with the farms and the main game for the boys was 'horses and horsemen'. The school had knitted bridles and one boy would be the 'horse' galloping around the playground under the control of a 'horseman' on the reins.

When I was seven my parents, despairing at my apparent lack of academic ability, sent me to a small boarding school in Ipswich. This was St Edmund's School, in a red brick Victorian house overlooking Christchurch Park. On my first night in the dormitory after lights out, the boys calculated who would be killed if a bomb fell in the garden. I was in the 'would be badly maimed' section, but fortunately Hitler didn't choose to attack the St Edmund's Road area of Ipswich during the remaining few months of the war.

The headmaster was an honest but unimaginative man called Mr McLintoc. He was a firm believer that small boys should be controlled and have their characters shaped by regular beatings. These were carried out in a cool and clinical manner every week when those who had broken the school's numerous rules solemnly lined up outside Mr McLintoc's study.

There was a carefully worked out set of rules governing the type of beating given for each offence. Under no circumstance was crying permitted, small boys who blubbed were ridiculed by the whole school. It was excellent training for any who expected to be physically tortured at some stage in their career. The school was run by Mrs Marshall, whose late husband had started St Edmund's. She was a real gem and thoroughly understood small boys and the way to control them with charm.

30. Harry Ferguson with Sir John Black on one of the original grey 'Fergie' tractors.

Everyone else at the school spoke a very different version of English to my basic country speech. Mrs Marshall would pat me on the head and say 'There there Simper, you are my little Suffolk dumpling!' It was a brilliant tactic, I suppressed my Suffolk speech in a matter of weeks.

Once, when my parents were taking me back to school in Ipswich, they gave an American airman a lift and when he got out, by way of thanks, he gave me two small packs of chewing gum. At school, word spread quickly that Simper was in possession of a banned substance. For possessing the dangerous American gum I was summoned to Mr McLintoc's study.

I expected to be beaten, but McLintoc was basically a fair man. I explained that the gum had been a gift from an American to my parents who had given a lift as part of the war effort. McLintoc recognised that it would have been rude not to have accepted the gum. As I had not dared to open the chewing gum packs I was not beaten, but they were confiscated and returned to me at the end of the term. When, many weeks later, I was finally given the gum, I was bitterly disappointed. All that trouble and it was tasteless.

Being an only child living on a lonely farm I spent much of my school holidays riding on the horses or tractors. My great hobby was killing rats and my partner in this was a tough little fox terrier called Fusser. He not only killed rats with great skill, but also ate them and then in the evenings lay in front of the farmhouse fire and made the most disgusting smells.

To begin with I used to kill the rats with a stick which ran riot over the corn barn and cow meal shed, but I graduated to an air gun and then a four ten shot-gun. When I first got my hammer four ten I crept into our black barn and spotted a rat sneaking up under the rafters. With my air gun I would have stopped him, but with the four ten I obliterated the rat and also blew a great hole in the tiled roof. To my horror I saw the blue sky and heard tiles crashing down outside. I hid my gun in the house and was very glad that I was going back to boarding school the next day.

Looking at the farm's wages book for 1948, it records the total labour bill for 24 people on 500 acres was £94 a week. At the time, head cowman Billy Beer was the top earner, taking home £6 7s 6d a week. About this time Billy bought a tiny square car and this was the major talking point in the local villages. A working man owning a car! Before this only the vicar, land agent, doctor and two farmers in Bawdsey owned cars. By 1998 I think there would have been at least 150 cars owned in Bawdsey.

No-one was in the least surprised that Bawdsey Estate controlled the villages it covered. Since the Anglo-Saxons first divided England up into estates, this was how rural areas were governed. The success of the estate system depended on whether each one was run by a wise lord or an arrogant waster. For those living on estates it could be heaven or hell, but most of the great land-owning families considered they had a responsibility to look after the tenantry on their estate, although they certainly could not treat them as equals.

The first blow against the great estates was struck in the Edwardian period by Lloyd George's Liberal Government. From then on, successive Governments in search of cash hacked away with taxes aimed at the inherited land-owners. The post-war Labour Government was desperate to raise capital to nationalise the main manufacturing industries, which included agriculture, a disastrous policy which did not save a single industry. Also this Government used Death Duty Tax to destroy the estates' control over the countryside.

This was really taking a sledge-hammer to crack a nut. Most of the estate owners thought of their private estates as an amenity and ran them as a hobby. Although they had rents collected for them, the emphasis was usually placed on hunting, shooting, gardening or collecting fine art, not that these private kingdoms should be run as profit-generating businesses.

The great nineteenth century estate owners had shaped the English landscape to suit their sporting and aesthetic tastes. Most of them wanted a nice view from their great country houses and the tenant farmers had considerable limitations imposed on them. After the death of a head of a great land-owning family, the arrival of the postman with the fateful and crippling tax demand meant that many long-established estates vanished from the maps.

Some large estates, much reduced in size (the Dukes of Bedford once had 400,000 acres, but this has come down to a mere 13,000 acres), adjusted and attempted to make a profit. Many of these estates are still in place and give a feeling of continuity to life in the countryside, but they have lost all their power over rural England. Control has passed to the elected councillors and to local government and the numerous pressure groups trying to influence events. Everyone is polite to the holders of the ancient titles, but local government does not take any account of their views. Although each elected member is only there for a few years, the owners of land are responsible for the countryside for much longer periods.

The super-rich still exist, but in this democratic age they can no longer create private kingdoms in the countryside. The new rich who have moved into the countryside keep a low profile. Most are content with a large house, paddocks for the horses and some land to plant trees or for a vineyard. They use their extreme wealth to buy a helicopter, super-yacht in the Med, a villa in the West Indies or some other way of generating privilege.

After 1951, the Bawdsey Estate was hit very hard by Death Dues. Before one tax demand had been settled another member of the family died so they got another crippling tax bill. Over the next decade the Estate was forced to sell four villages and it ceased to be a power in local politics.

Most of the houses were sold off very cheaply, often to the local people living in them. One elderly former Estate farm foreman arrived at the Estate Office with a bag of gold sovereigns, the profit from his siphoning off produce during the World War I, and demanded to buy his cottage. The impact on the social structure of the district was even more dramatic. In time, the former homes of ploughmen and marshmen became weekend cottages and then the much desired residences of office workers from nearby towns.

The Estate had been at the centre of all local activities and many people were, for a time, bewildered by the sale of so much of it. In Bawdsey the Estate had provided a Reading Room, the upright Edwardian ideal was that working men should not go to the pub in the evening and then be late for work the next day, but should sit in the 'Club Room' and read an improving book. The two farmers in the village, Jim Mann and my father, bought the Reading Room and presented it to the village to keep a central meeting place.

The inauguration of the Bawdsey Cricket Club was another idea intended to improve the quality of life. The Estate had provided the ground and pavilion, and when new balls and bats were needed someone would go up to the estate office and ask for them. When the Estate had sold its last house in the village the residents suddenly had to support their own cricket and Recreation Ground. Most rallied around to help raise the cash, but some men refused to pay a 'sub' to the cricket club, they could not adjust to the idea of paying for their own hobby. That was something the rich had always done.

Chapter Six

GOOD LUCK IN YOUR CAREER

FARM. AN AREA OF LAND AND ITS BUILDINGS
UNDER ONE MANAGEMENT
FOR RAISING CROPS OR LIVESTOCK
Oxford Dictionary

I left school in the summer of 1953 and started work on my father's farm. It seemed a very good time to be going into agriculture as mechanisation was taking away the endless drudgery of working the land, while the Government, desperate to end food rationing, were putting money into developing British agriculture. My father had just bought Manor Farm, Bawdsey from the Bawdsey Estate, then crippled by Death Dues. The farm had been bought at the high price of £65 an acre, and an extra hundred acres of grazing marshes at £51 an acre were also added.

While these negotiations were going on, a combination of gale-force winds and a very high tide resulted in the river walls being breached and the River Deben, normally a mile away, was lapping at the bottom of the garden. About half the area which had just been purchased went under salt water and was not farmable again for several years. This was not a total disaster, because after the 1953 Floods the Government made payments to help get the land back into production. I believe sugar was still on ration then, and imported wheat was costing foreign currency. However, in order to get this aid the grassland had to be ploughed up, in the drive to make Britain self-sufficient in food.

There was a great deal of parental worrying about borrowing so much money to buy the farm and whether it would ever be possible to pay it back. At that time the financial side of the farm seemed remote to me. My main aim was simply to learn how to drive a tractor and back a four-wheeled trailer. There were still two Suffolk horses on the farm, Scot and Major, but I only worked with them once. Because the Hanging Six Acres field was very wet and tractors could not get on it I went with Walter Halls to cart sugar beet off with a horse pulling a one ton tumbrel.

The horse, a powerful Suffolk, was very slow, but the great advantage was that on the command 'up a step!' it walked forward until you shouted 'wow' and then it stopped. No-one has yet trained a tractor to do that.

The business of working the horse was jealously guarded by Walter Halls, the Head Horseman, or to be more accurate the only horseman. He need not have worried, I made a point of not knowing how to work a horse. Nor did any of the young men. Our aim was to be allocated one of the farm's four low-powered tractors. Walking behind a horse was for the 'old buggers'.

I had lived on a farm all my life, but found the working routine very difficult to adjust to. At the beginning of each school term we had been given a timetable so that for the next few weeks we knew exactly where we would be at any time of the day. There was no timetable for farming, it was simply a matter of playing it by ear and every day was dictated by the weather. At school there were rules for everything and the headmaster and his staff battled hard to make sure they were obeyed. There really did not seem to be any rules

31. David Mann and Robert with his terrier Fusser on the Valley field, Ramsholt, 1950. In the background is the first trailed Claas combine.

to farming, but there was an unwritten set of local customs which could not be broken and the rest was down to instinct.

Just after I left school Tom Stanley, who farmed in Occold, wished me every success in my career in the agricultural industry. At the time I was spending every bleak winter's day with Fred Garnham and a little grey Fergie tractor carting sugar beet tops through a sea of mud to feed the dairy herd. It had not occurred to me that this was anything so grand as 'a career in an industry'.

I actually started just before harvest and one of my first jobs was helping with 'opening up' a field of wheat by hand so that the tractor pulling the binder did not run down the headland. In the usual farm way this was all very casual. To start with, nobody could remember where the scythes had been stored. We searched the cart-shed, looking up in the rafters under the thatch, then in some old wartime Nissan huts. Everyone we met kindly offered some advice as to where they had last been seen, which all proved to be incorrect. Finally, the scythes were found hanging up in the garden shed and everyone said 'oh yes, that is where we left them after we scythed the orchard.'

We set off walking down a track to the wheat on the Seven Acre field. The two young men, Nobby Burch and Dougie Andrews, walked ahead with scythes over their shoulders, followed by 'Gouby' Driver, who had just left school and started work on the farm, and myself, last and definitely least, carrying the stones for sharpening the scythes.

Once on the field, we boys were treated to a brief lecture by the men about their prowess with a scythe and how things had been different when they had started work.

Nobby talked about the time when he had started at Fiske's on Virtues Farms in the thir-

32. Harvest gang Manor Farm, 1954. Left to right Robert, 'Mo' Malster, Dougie Andrews, Fred Garnham and Walter Halls.

33. Harvest gang on a little grey 'Fergie' at Manor Farm, 1954. Fred Garnham driving, Walter Halls, Mo Malster, Dougie Andrews, 'Gouby' Driver and Nobby Burch.

ties when the 'shoeing the cob' custom was still carried out. In this barbaric initiation ritual the boys were taken into the barn where a wagon rope was thrown over a beam. Nobby said he knew what was coming, so he quickly agreed to buy the men a gallon of beer, but one boy refused. The men hoisted his foot up in the air and started driving a 6 inch nail into the sole of his hob-nailed boot.

Nobby leant on his scythe handle and recalled with a laugh 'It wan't long afore the old boy howled out he'd buy them beer!'

Without any more reminisces Nobby and Dougie set off rhythmically mowing around the outside of the field to make room for the binder. Gouby and I followed behind, bundling up the loose straw into 'shuffs' (sheaves). We did not use string to tie up the shuffs, but the straw itself. The whole process was pure Victorian. By the afternoon it was very sunny and the hard manual work had made us thirsty.

We were only one field away from the Bawdsey 'Star', so Gouby, who at fifteen seemed to already be on good terms with the landlord, was dispatched off to buy beer. When he returned with the bottles of beer we sat under the shade of a huge elm tree drinking it out of Cobbold's pint bottles. As we were being paid 'day work' there did not seem to be a great hurry to finish cutting around the field.

Later, the binder arrived to cut the wheat and the whole field was left covered in small heaps of shuffs. This was a serious start to the Harvest and all the men on the farm, apart from the cowmen, now arrived and we picked up the shuffs in pairs and stood them in 'shocks', so that they could be dried out ready for carting. In those days corn was often cut while still a little green and left to ripen in the shocks. The Seven Acres wheat had been 'clean' with few weeds, but the neighbouring Meadows barley field had a lot of thistles in it.

We started shocking this field just after seven in the morning, after the men had packed their bikes under the shadow of Grove Wood, and about eight of us walked into the field. The corn was still damp with 'dag' (dew) and this quickly soaked through our clothes, but worse still, the prickly dead thistle went right through into our arms.

Looking back, there was one of the gang I wish I had talked to. His real name was Charles Weavers, but everyone called him 'Charlie Wiffers' and he was held in high regard. Charlie Wiffers must have been in his seventies, a small man with white hair and a drooping moustache and slightly hump-backed after years of manual labour. I was later told that he had been Head Horseman, before semi-retiring, and had worked on the farm for most of his life. He must have been able to remember these fields back in the 1890s. Little had changed since then.

Once we got under the elm trees, Walter Burch looked up and wondered why the leaves were dying. None of us had an answer, but over the next decades all these trees died of Dutch Elm Disease. Once the trees had gone, the field boundaries were often just ploughed away.

At the time, everyone clearly remembered the food shortages of the war years, and there was still a great national push to increase food production. In Britain it had been just that, a 'shortage of food', unlike the mainland European countries where in World War II a large section of the community had experienced near starvation. After this bleak experience, these countries were very keen to protect food-producers.

My father had already bought a combine-harvester which was being used on the two farms in Ramsholt. This was a silver Claas with ex-aeroplane tyres and a man on the top tying up the coombe sacks of corn which were then carted back to the barn. Everyone was

34. Harvest gang at Manor Farm, Bawdsey with 'Gouby' Driver on the three-wheeled Allis-Chalmers petrol-TVO tractor 1954. This Allis-Chalmers, like the John Deere, had been imported as part of the war effort. The three wheels were designed for working in the rows of the cotton crops in the southern United States.

delighted with the progress of machines on the farms, glad to get rid of the long hours of slavery which had gone with working horses.

The first combine was not large enough to cut all the corn, so for a few years much more was still cut by a binder, then carted and stacked near the farmyard and threshed during the winter. Before I left school the 'thrashing tackle' had been driven by a steam traction engine. A slow running brute which poured out black smoke and was presided over by the kindly Mr Burrows. Apparently his father, 'One Arm' Burrows, had driven the same engine and was renowned on the farms for being able, with just the one arm, to pick up a live rat by its tail and throw it straight into the fire-box.

Later, the threshing tackle was driven by a John Deere D tractor on a pulley belt, but it was still a hard, dirty job. Gouby got the worst job 'taking off the colder'. This was the corn husk which came out at the side of the threshing drum in a cloud of dust. By the end of the day he was completely black. I got the second worst job, in the 'bully hole'. This was up on the stack underneath the 'pitcher' which brought the loose threshed straw up from the 'drum'. All day straw fell on my head and I fought manfully to pass the straw on to the 'stacker', who was undertaking the skilled job of building the stack.

I remember one bitterly cold winter's day in the bully hole threshing some barley stacks at Walk Barn, Ramsholt when the wind blew the straw and piercing havels into my face and I could hardy keep my eyes open.

'Don't keep astopping to wipe yu' eyes, boy' pleaded the stacker, worried that his work-

53

35. Robert and Fred Garnham bull training, Manor Farm, Bawdsey in about 1955.

36. Part of the Bawdsey herd of British Friesians in the cow shed at Ramsholt Lodge about 1954.

mates would think he was doing a bad job 'We an't got the time to dawdle up here, just get the old straw across to me a bit quicker. I gotter keep my old corner high!'

At four o'clock the welcome sound of the drum slowing down was heard and the last straw fell at my feet. We stuck the pitchforks into the stack and climbed down the ladder. The whole threshing gang of eight men came to inspect the straw stack and the stacker was congratulated on being able to build a really straight stack in the high winds, but I sank against the ladder totally exhausted.

Within a few years a second combine was purchased and the binders were sold and the war-time tractors left as well. One of the new replacements was an International Farmall tractor from the United States, which was twice as fast as the old Fordsons and the wonderful John Deere D. The young tractor-drivers at Ramsholt took to tractor racing at 15mph around the stack and the foreman Frank Ling was in despair at how to control the situation. Finally he hit on the solution and got my father to send the Farmall away and have the top gears removed to make it as slow as the other tractors. They had rather missed the point about mechanisation. From now on if you wanted to stay in farming, everything had to go faster and get steadily larger.

The new 30hp Fordson Major tractors arrived at the time we started to 'bust up' the open grass marshes which had been killed by the salt water flooding in 1953. Government advisers had been around and said that these must not be returned to grass, but cultivated for wheat or some other cereal crop. This land had never been ploughed before, so alone on a tractor on the wide open marshes it was like busted-up virgin prairie. In March a raw wind blew in from the North Sea and sitting there on a tractor open to the elements, going up and down the field, it was very difficult to keep warm, even covered in sacks.

Great care had to be taken in selecting the right sacks for warmth. The heavy coombe sacks were alright if you were sitting on a tractor, but for keeping the wind out while cutting cabbage the lighter sugar beet pulp sacks were just the job.

'It's a lazy wind' the old hands laughed, 'goes right through you afore it goes around!'

Although I enjoyed tractor driving, I was never any good with machinery maintenance and was happier working with animals. This meant I became relief cowman when any of the three people working with the herd were away. Back in 1947 my father had decided to switch from his rather mixed herd of shorthorns and red poll cows into an attested herd of pedigree British Friesians which gave more milk. By the time I left school he was pushing this further and trying to build up a reputation for selling pedigree British Friesian bulls.

Promising cows and young bulls had to be trained to lead in the show ring. Fred Garnham and I, under Head Cowman Billy Beer's instructions, would slip a halter on to a couple of young bulls and train them to be led. This was real buckoo stuff, and the first time out the young bull would come charging out of the box completely wild. From the first moment it was a battle of wits with the bulls, they were always much stronger than a man and at any time they could have knocked someone down.

I received several injuries, and still have damaged toes resulting from bulls treading on my right foot. Another time when I thought I had won the trust of a young bull and was carelessly leading him out of a box on a long rein, he suddenly swung his head round and hit me in the chest. The impact was like being hit with a brick wall. Gasping with pain, I fell back against the wall. I learned the lesson that you should never trust animals, they have no rules about being kind to humans, it is only we who feel we should be kind to them.

After a few weeks, the bulls would calm down and happily go for their daily walk. It was a great triumph to be able to walk the animals up Bawdsey Street and stop and talk to people. In the end, we had a bull weighing over a ton which would do exactly what we commanded with a quiet word and jerk on the halter. The bulls were led by a halter and rope on the nose ring. Without the ring in the nose it would have been impossible to control these huge, powerful animals. A slight tug on the ring was painful and made the bull behave himself. Using a ring was really the last resort, because if it was used too much it enraged the animal. If the bull lost his temper, nothing would stop him. The neck of a bull is tremendously powerful and if enraged they can knock a man down and crush him to death in a matter of seconds.

In fact we controlled these huge animals with a mixture of calculated kindness and bluff. The only time I was in really serious trouble with a bull, bluff saved me. I had been to look at some winter wheat on the Peyton Hall marshes and thought I would take a short-cut back through a meadow near the buildings. I was not bothered that a bull was standing with some heifers on the other side of the meadow, but the bull was bothered by me. Perhaps he was defending his heifers, or maybe my loose duffel coat flapping in the wind had upset him.

Suddenly, I heard the heavy thunder of a bull galloping straight towards me. I had nothing to defend myself with so I turned and walked straight towards the on-coming bull shouting in heavy basic farmyard language that if he came one step nearer I would kill

37. Billy Beer with a Friesian bull at Manor Farm, Bawdsey about 1956.

him. The bull was completely amazed and swung round and stopped. I walked towards him shouting wildly, the bull lowered his head, but retreated. Once he did this I started to move backwards toward the safety of a fence as quickly as I dared without running. The bull came on again, I stopped again and started swearing loudly at him. We did this several times and each time the bull came a little nearer to me, testing to see if I really could hurt him. The last time he pulled up roaring with anger, head down a few feet from me, close enough for me to see the red of his eyes as he pawed the ground. It was now or never, so I ran the last few yards and threw myself under the bottom strand of a barbed wire fence.

The bull's head was down, smashing up the ground just behind me. I peered up from the bottom of a water-filled ditch, the bull had the power to flatten the barbed-wire fence and kill me, but he turned and trotted back to his heifers roaring with triumph.

The highlight of the bull-taming years was the Norwich Bull Sale in the early winter. By then, I was driving the 7 ton petrol Bedford lorry which we could attach a cattle float to. I would arrive at Manor Farm at 5am to find Billy Beer had already been there for some time, getting his charges into halters. In the still of the cold morning air the young bulls were led, one by one, up into the cattle float and tied up. Then Billy would climb into the passenger seat and roll himself yet another fag as I started the two hour drive to Norwich.

As we drove through the East Anglian countryside it was very noticeable that lights were on in the farmhouses and cottages, while everyone else was still firmly in bed. Billy had done this trip many times, so he knew the way into the centre of Norwich where the market was held on Castle Hill. We proudly led our young bulls out to their stalls and washed them down to remove any muck they had acquired on the journey. The bulls always seemed to enjoy this pandering to their appearance.

Then we made a quick visit to the cafe at the top of the hill for a cup tea and fried break-fast. While we were eating Billy, in a low tone so that we could not be overheard, sized up

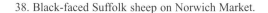

38. Black-faced Suffolk sheep on Norwich Market.

the opposition. Our great rival from the Sandlings peninsula was Mrs Martha Barton's Sutton Hoo herd of British Friesians. Billy, very loyal to our Bawdsey herd, would explain why the Sutton Hoo herd was overrated, but all the same they usually won more prizes at the show before the sale than our young bulls.

Back in the market Mrs Barton, a forceful and wealthy women with a driving passion for her Friesian herd, would sweep down the cattle lines past our bulls without even giving them a glance. Martha Barton had exacting standards, once at her regular watering-hole, the upstairs bar of the 'Crown and Anchor' at Ipswich, she ordered her 'usual' and the barman committed the sin of handing her a single whiskey. With a quick wrist action she flicked the whiskey back all over the barman and dryly commented 'my usual is ALWAYS a double'.

The shows and sales were the highlights, but the cowshed work was very much more down-to-earth. In the early 1950s the cows still slept outside all winter and it was the junior cowman's job to go and find them out on the meadows. At 5.30am we would go out into a sea of mud behind the cowshed and set off to find the herd in the pitch dark, while the raw cold wind blew in across the marshes. The cows usually found a hedge where they could shelter from the wind, but when they heard the call they would set off to the cow-shed, in the worst winter's weather with snow frozen to their backs.

I had missed the famous extreme winter of 1947, although I remember snow-drifts blocking the roads for weeks and when the snow finally thawed in the spring all the marshes were flooded. They still talked about that winter on the farm. They had to cut the cabbages by hand to be sent by road to Covent Garden Market in London. By February, the post-war food shortage was so bad that they went back yet again to cut more of the remaining leaves off the stalks and bagged those up for sale in London.

In the worst winter weather we were still cutting cabbages. One man went ahead with a broom, sweeping the snow off, two men bent double sliced the cabbages off with 'noppers' and the rest of us packed them into bags. At the end of the day, the bags of cabbages were carted off and loaded on to the lorry for London. By then I was loading our Foden lorry for its nightly run to Covent Garden or Spitalfields Markets. Arthur Potter drove the Foden to London and I was in trouble if the load slipped on the way. It was all right stacking bags of carrots and parsnips, but the cabbages and greens in bags were often loosely packed and the load moved. Once a less than happy Arthur returned to say that the corner of a load had slipped off and he had had to restack it on Melton Hill.

In the spring we worked the spring greens, by moving across the field snapping off the greens with our hands and stuffing them into bags. This was in the days before waterproof gloves, so it paid to keep moving to keep our hands warm.

As it was early spring, the pheasants were laying eggs and we often came across the nests. 'Good grub, boys!' old Bob Barker would cry out and would break a raw egg into one of his huge dirty hands and eat it straight down. Bob had grown up in Alderton before World War I when poverty meant the boys ate anything they could find in the hedgerows. That generation worked on the land and lived off it.

Ten years later, Bob was still with us when one day we were loading freshly cut hay bales. I say 'we', but actually Bob was leaning on his fork while I did all the lifting. I protested that the bales were heavy on my own, but Bob snapped me down. 'Hold you hard! Do you know how old I am?' he roared defiantly, 'at my time of life can you expect me to lift them heavy bales?'

When I asked Bob why he still came to work if he was drawing the pension, Bob said

39. Arthur Potter on the new Foden lorry with Nobby Burch and Walter Hall loading cabbages ready to go up to London overnight, 1952.

gruffly he needed the money, but I think he came out of force of habit. It could be a very long day sitting about waiting for the 'Swan' or the 'Crown' in Alderton to open. Bob was really the last of the labourers on that farm, men who had a knack of working with hand tools. I would rush in and use up all my energy, but the labourers would work all day at a steady pace. Never hurrying and never tiring, but always moving slowly forward.

Each morning Arthur Potter returned from the London markets and reported on the night's work. He often had trouble with lorries parking in the way, or with porters. The porters were paid threepence for every package they handled, but at some markets they sat playing cards in a back room while the lorry drivers did the unloading, although they still expected to be 'given a drink' for each lorry which was unloaded. No-one dared question the porters, as most of them appeared to be ex-boxers or wrestlers. If they were offended and they went out on strike it took considerable police presence to get the lorries through the picket lines.

Once a year I went with my father to visit the stand holders he loaded to at Covent Garden and Spitalfields, two of the five London wholesale fruit and vegetable markets. It was a tough life for the salesmen and porters at the wholesale markets, as they started work at about 4.30am. By about 10am the day's selling was over and everyone was ready to go home and sleep.

40. Some of the people who worked on Manor Farm, an arable and dairy farm, in 1959. In 1999 the same farm had three people involved in arable farming and outdoor pigs. Left to right: Nobby Burch, Bert Last, Billy Beer, Peggy Beer, Mrs Pratt, Mo Malster, Alf Grimsey, Peter Ransby, Dougie Andrews, Walter Hall, Andy Pratt, Mrs Burch, Walter Burch, Bill Read, Doreen Barber, Vic Clouting and Arthur Potter. Centre kneeling is Bob Barker and Norman Simper is on the right. This group includes a carpenter and bricklayer who worked full-time repairing cottages and farm buildings.

On A.J. Edwards' stand at Covent Garden the Cockney salesmen said 'it's pneumonia corner 'ere, wind cuts down 'ere something awful in the winter, nobody lives to a great age who works 'ere!'

Outside, the street was covered in vegetables which had fallen off the lorries while the porters unloaded them, while parked vehicles almost blocked the roads as other vans and lorries slowly wound their way through. The whole scene was organised chaos.

There was a properly covered market at 'The Garden', but at Spitalfields wholesale fruit and vegetable sales took place in narrow streets. Here we visited Sutton and Kirkman, whose stand was a small warehouse with vegetables stacked in piles overflowing on to the street outside.

Mr Sutton was a round, jolly man who appeared to enjoy the banter which went on with selling to shop-owners and barrow-boys. Mr Kirkman, a tall elderly man of great charm, was every inch an English gentleman in a smart grey pin-striped suit. At first glance he looked a bit out of place as a vegetable salesman on a London street, but he had spent his whole working life there. Mr Kirkman told me that his family had been farmers in Essex when he had started by driving to London overnight and selling the vegetables straight off their horse-drawn wagon. The 'stand' was literally where the wagon had stood. Our cabbages, carrots, parsnips and spring greens were all sold 'on commission', the higher the price the more commission the stand-holders and salesmen took. We all wanted a 'good trade' and hoped some well-meaning journalist would report a shortage. If a newspaper reported a shortage of carrots, everyone went out and bought them and the price would shoot up. When there was a good growing season and vegetables were plentiful, people got fed up with them quickly and prices would drop.

Vegetable-growers are really gamblers, making a fortune one year, making a loss the next two years and then growing more to try and make back the loss. Big vegetable-growers and packers can in a few months lose everything and suddenly huge companies can vanish from the farming scene.

In the 1950s, when I worked with a gang, harvesting by hand, the price of vegetables paid by the London greengrocers, market stall-holders and barrow-boys seemed as remote as the moon. In the thin winter's daylight we worked across the fields bent over in the bitter cold wind, with sacks wrapped around our waists for warmth, cutting and bagging vegetables which the next day would appear on the dinnerplates of hundreds of Londoners.

Head cowman Billy Beer with the bull Lavenham Skipper at Manor Farm, Bawdsey, 1956.

The Walk Barn and open cattle fattening yard shortly before being pulled down in 1970. This Ramsholt field barn was built in an optimistic period in the nineteenth century when high cereal prices led to the ploughing up of the sheep walks. However organic style of cereal growing relied on inflated prices and very large numbers of low paid hand workers and once these finished it became unsustainable.

Arthur Potter and Walter Burch loading cabbages on the Green, Ramsholt in 1951. This petrol 7 ton Bedford lorry went up to London's Covent Garden over night. Robert, with his beloved dog Fusser is next to Norman Simper. Vegetable growing at this time led to the Suffolk Sandlings being known as the 'Gold Coast'

Chapter Seven

LETTERS FROM THE PAST

THE BEST MANURE
IS THE FARMER'S BOOT
Nineteenth century farm management advice

In 1959 Pearl and I were married and went to live in a cottage at Ramsholt, a wild and unwelcoming place, full of old people living in derelict cottages. We later heard that some local people thought we would only stay one winter in a cold damp cottage at the end of a long muddy lane. They had a point, winter in the open bleak countryside is totally differ-ent to winter in the towns, but forty years later we are still here.

The cottage's only claim to fame was its plum trees, some green ancient variety, and its well which we were told had special powers. In the past, people had sailed down from Woodbridge and given the old lady in the cottage a penny for a glass of the special water. European standards have since stated that our well-water, which we have drunk safely for four decades, has to be treated. Perhaps it was the trip in the open air on the attractive river which made the water seem so special.

The parish was made up of wide open fields with woods planted for pheasant-shooting by the Bawdsey Estate. The place had a feeling of being doomed, this part of the estate was up for sale and most of the potential buyers were interested in pheasant-shooting, not house-repairing. This was in the 'slum clearance' era and the mood of the age was to tear down all old buildings.

Over the next decade, as the old people died off, down came their cottages. Elizabethan long houses and eighteenth century Suffolk brick houses were all levelled to the ground and brambles grew over the sites. The new owner's farm manager said briskly that in the future no-one would want to live in such a remote place. People had to be rehoused in the neighbouring village of Shottisham because it had a shop (now long gone) and the bus called there. Besides, the people living in Ramsholt interfered with the pheasant-shooting.

I wondered about the history of this tiny parish on the edge of nowhere. At the time no one knew (or cared) very much about the parish's past, but more recent research has shown that the area along the eastern bank of the River Deben has in fact been inhabited for about five thousand years. The clues to the parish's distant past were in the fields which I was helping to work, but I could not interpret these.

Aerial photographs taken during the very dry summer of 1976 showed that the whole Sandlings peninsula between the Rivers Deben and Alde were covered in crop marks. These crop marks were the trackways, field boundaries and hut sites of the Iron Age peo-ple who had lived here in well-organised communities before the Romans arrived.

It has taken field walking by John Newman of the Suffolk Archaeology Unit to find and date the pottery on the settlement sites scattered around the area. The most interesting early history has been unearthed by two metal-detector enthusiasts. Building site con-troller Roy Damant and school cleaner Brian Warren have spent countless winter days combing the fields with metal-detectors. Their results are astounding.

In their search for the past, Roy and Brian walk the fields after rain, looking for pottery which marks likely settlement sites, and then home in on these areas with metal-detectors. A slow, plodding task, often in the biting east wind which the coast is renowned for. On one settlement site near springs they made a major find, eighteen rare gold Treasure Trove coins from around 50BC. Most of these were the British coins of the Tiviant tribe, the Sandlings area was their boundary with Iceni to the north.

Roy stuck lucky once before, when in 1987 at Sutton he found a hoard of silver Roman Republican coins, hidden in some crisis, but never retrieved by their original owner. The tiny battered jewellery he found on ring ditch sites suggests the tribal Iron Age people were living here within sight of the Roman fort guarding the Deben mouth.

The Roman garrison at Walton had failed to keep out the Anglo-Saxons who came across the North Sea to raid and then settle, creating the new kingdom of East Anglia. The Iron Age people favoured the open heathland where no doubt they grazed their sheep. The early Anglo-Saxons were very much boat people, keeping up a link with their old home-land in northern Europe, and they liked to be near tidal waters. The villages along the Deben valley mostly have names which go back to the Anglo-Saxons. Bawdsey may have been Baldere's Island, while the new Anglo-Saxon village on a sheltered creek just up the tidal estuary became known as Ram's Holt, literally Ram's Wood, which suggests the first people here were of Danish origin.

All that remains now of the Anglo-Saxon village is the Church. It is likely that Ramsholt Church, like several others in the Sandlings, is sited on the place of pagan religious prac-tices. When Pope Gregory sent missionaries to convert the 'Angles' to Christianity he instructed that to make the conversion easier the old customs and sites should be used. People would accept the new Christian faith if it occupied the old place of religious impor-tance. Ramsholt has always been a rather poor place and while the other churches were rebuilt in the medieval period, this one retains its curious oval tower now so beloved by tourists and film-makers.

It was the church which had divided England up into parishes, it made administration possible and the collection of the tithe (the church tax) easier. The King was keen to make tax-gathering possible, but also wanted to raise armies so the working countryside was divided up into manors. Each manor was required to pay a fixed amount to the King and to supply a fixed number of fighting men. The Lords of the Manor held manorial courts to sort out local disputes. In East Anglia, after the Viking invasion, there were several manors to one village and Ramsholt became two manors.

The Manor of Ramsholt was around the church while the Manor of Peyton, which had a moated manor house, was to the south, near springs at the head of another creek. In the twelfth century Reginald de Peyton lived at Peyton Hall, and his family later held other manors in the area and obtained the right to hold a market at Bawdsey. They were impor-tant enough to get their coat of arms on the gateway of the Butley Abbey.

Peyton Hall was badly damaged by fire and a new square Victorian house was built on to its front. In 1962 the owners decided to rip down the old medieval part of Peyton Hall and replace it with a flat-roofed characterless extension (which later had problems with leaking). Frank Ling, who was living in the house at this time, said 'I don't know what the fuss is all about, those old carved beams aren't much. I could do them myself if you gave me some tools.'

He showed me where the plasterwork had been ripped off the inside of the house to expose those carved medieval oak beams, as hard as iron. Next day, workmen burned most of these old timbers, but I managed to save some of the carvings and later had Ipswich

Museum date them to the period between 1430-70. At the time it was pulled down this old medieval manor house was considered to be completely worthless. If it was put up for sale today, it would appear on the glossy advert pages of *Country Life* with a very hefty price-tag.

Peyton Hall was a rich manor because it was sited on light land which was easy to work with a plough drawn by oxen, but the soil only held moisture in the early summer growing period. However, the sheep grazing on the vast area of open heathland just inland were the main source of wealth. Because sheep can go for long periods without drinking, they could graze on the miles of open heathland, although there was a problem during the long hot summers when all the vegetation on the very sandy soil died off. The Lords of the Manors had to find a way to feed their flocks in the summer. They did this by throwing up dirt banks, river walls, keeping tidal waters off the former saltings and creating the grass marshes on which livestock could graze at the height of summer.

Several attempts were made over the centuries to finally wall back the Deben to its main channel. The two miles of river wall between Peyton Hall and Bawdsey created around 1,000 acres of summer grazing. This was a major piece of engineering, it must have been a great day when the gangs of labourers working with shovels finally closed the gap.

Quite when all this walling took place is very difficult to ascertain, the first walls were probably started by the Anglo-Saxons, and later the medieval Lords of the Manor built walls further out and the walling was probably finished off by the Elizabethans. When we first moved to the parish the old people used to say they had been told that sailors had once rowed to get water from the springs at Ramsholt Street. That would have meant rowing over the Dock Marshes where our cattle later grazed. That creek must have been walled off several centuries before and the folk memory carried on so long as there was a local population to pass on the story.

The reason the village around the church was abandoned is not certain. Many medieval hamlets appear to have gone around the time of the Black Death Plague in 1348-49. Certainly, the village disappeared around this time, but it may have been because a different way of working the land was adopted. Most of the Lords of the Manor and the manorial tenants had undertaken sheep farming, but in the seventeenth century the Wool Trade, the 'old draperies', declined. The new Tudor landowners wanted their tenants to produce more cereal crops which could be sold in the steadily growing towns. Certainly, around 1600 about six small half-timbered long houses, homes for yeoman farmers, were built dotted around the edge of Ramsholt sheep walks.

The parish had been connected to the outside world by a series of tracks across the sheep walks. Parts of the ancient trackway remained as deep farm roads leading to empty fields which were once settlements. Defined public roads started to be used and by the Victorian period the making up of the public roads became the responsibility of each parish. In East Suffolk, gangs of women and children used to pick up flints in the fields, which were then used to make up the roads.

The food shortages during the Napoleonic Wars and the period until the Repeal of the Corn Laws gave a great boost to cereal farming. The land-owners, sure of good rents, began to plant hawthorn hedges to turn some of the sheep walks into arable fields for corn-growing. New farm buildings and field barns were also put up and wells were sunk so that rows of workers' cottages could be built. These new cottages, built with brick from local kilns, were scattered around the parish so that the men and women did not have too far to walk to work. During this period most of the Sandlings farmhouses were enlarged and acquired gardens and lawns and smart new riding stables to house the farmer's carriage and fine horses. Some farmers even started planting trees in fields near their houses to create parkland similar to that around the gentry's grand houses. All paid for by the high corn prices.

The Sandlings became a very progressive area because the farms were large enough for the farmers to experiment with new crops and ideas. The Suffolk horse was most developed by breeders in the Sandlings. In 1836, Samuel Richardson of Peyton Hall won a prize for his hand-threshing machine, a wonderful device worked by two men with a sort of rowing action. This did not provide the answer to the time-consuming threshing on the barn floor with a flail, but a few years later there were horse-driven threshing machines and after that the steam-driven threshing drum. Later in the nineteenth century, simple machines were being produced by local manufacturers in the drive to cut down the huge cost of labour needed on the arable farms.

As grain prices fell, people left in search of work in the new industrial towns. There had not been an exodus on this scale since the Wool Trade collapsed in the sixteenth century, when people left for New England.

Ramsholt's population dropped from 202 in 1851 down to 132 by 1881 and some of the older cottages disappeared from the map. The same was happening in all the other Sandlings villages, in neighbouring Alderton it fell from 620 in 1844 down to 426 by 1921. Still, Alderton had two public houses and on a Saturday the men got full of beer and then had fights in the village streets.

Ramsholt had its own pub, the 'Blue Anchor', but when the railways started to bring summer visitors to the area Lord Rendlesham moved the licence down to the Dock Farm

41. These horses were used on an East Anglian farm until 1958.

farmhouse near the river and called it the 'Ramsholt Arms'. In 1879, a school was built in the Street and this had to be enlarged in 1913 when there were fifty-eight children attending. There was also a small shop and a nonconformist chapel in a cottage and it looked as if, after centuries of neglect, the parish was going to develop into a full-blown village. Unfortunately, the agricultural depression of the inter-war years dealt the area a terrible economic blow from which it never recovered.

Life for the country people had always been hard. Mrs Rush, who had lived in our cottage, remembered being sent out to work in 1900 when she was eleven. Children of that age would have earned a few pennies leading the great Suffolk horses and wagons back from the harvest fields. This was very dangerous, because the great animals often lifted the young children right off the ground. There was nothing golden about these brutal rural communities, but everyone was in the same boat and usually they helped one another.

The harvests were a time when everyone worked long hours, but they were not paid overtime. Before the harvest the men would form a Harvest Company and contract with the farmer to 'take the harvest' for a set sum. If the weather was dry the men could cut and stack corn quickly, earning more than a day's wage. If wet, they could be out of pocket.

The Harvest Company elected their own foremen, the Harvest Lord and Lady (both men), from among their number. George Green, a labourer in Shottisham, told me he 'took a harvest' in 1909 for nine pounds and nine shillings. If a man came to work late then the Lord of the Harvest fined him and if boys fooled around they were picked up and had their bottoms banged against a wagon-side.

42. Suffolk horses in a stackyard on a January day in 1958.

The farmers, if they felt the work was not going fast enough, would send out the maids with flagons of beer. After this the men, often in a drunken stupor, worked at twice the speed, singing and shouting as they went. However, if too much beer arrived work stopped completely. Charlie Malster, who as a boy in the 1920s started with a gang scything peas near Ramsholt Lodge, remembered the men so drunk that they ended the day asleep in the hedge. Another Harvest Company scything barley on Alderton Mount got so overcome by beer with gin in it that they threw down their scythes and had a race to see who could roll to the bottom of the hill first.

When I started in the 1950s the old men recalled how the last load from the harvest field was called the 'Horkey', and how when they were boys this wagon and its horse would be decorated with branches and even flags. After this came a drunken supper known as a Harvest Horkey and then, on Sunday, some of the men went to church or chapel with their families and soberly sang 'All is Safely Gathered In.'

In the 1970s we had more glimpses of the past in a series of visits and letters from ladies who had grown up in the parish before World War I. They all talked of an extraordinarily happy, if slightly Spartan, childhood here. First came one of the Pettitt family who had lived in our cottage from about 1889 to 1925. Samuel Pettitt had got a job with Sir Cuthbert Quilter as head horseman and his daughter said she was one of nine children. I said innocently, 'how on earth did you all squash in here?' 'My dear' said the former Miss Pettitt with pride, 'when we were first here it was three cottages and we just had one room up and down at the far end!'

The 'Far End' was a tiny brick one-up, one down cottage which had been added on to the end of a small 1600 Suffolk long house. It appears the Quilters took pity on Pettitt and converted the three cottages into one.

43. Mr Burr on his horse in about 1903. He was Bawdsey Estate's agent on Ramsholt Lodge. The farmhouse was pulled down in 1962.

44. Twenty-six Suffolk horses at Ramsholt Lodge in about 1903. There were twenty-eight horses needed to work some 500 acres of arable light land.

'When we were children we used to look out of the bedroom window in the summer and see otters playing by the creek', recalled our visitor, 'do they still do that?' Sadly, in 1959 I had found the last otter, shot dead by a gamekeeper, lying beside the creek.

This lady also recalled the 1904 floods when the tide was 6ft higher than normal. Evidently a sailing barge floated up on top of Ramsholt Dock quay. Her brother had been walking back from Sutton along the Shottisham Creek river wall when he heard the roar of the water as the wall burst behind him and the tide flooded out on to the grazing marshes. He ran the last stretch home.

The next glimpse of a very different childhood came from Lorna Burr, whose father had been agent for Quilter at Ramsholt Lodge between 1900-06. Sir Cuthbert Quilter had doubtless 'taken the farm in hand' because he could not find a tenant and I have no doubt it was being run at a loss just to keep the village people in employment.

Lorna Burr's father, as the landowner's representative, was very concerned with keeping the small church going. The living was so poor that the church had to be linked to another parish. In 1862 Ramsholt was combined with Waldringfield across the river. The Rev. Henry Canham used to be rowed across. The Ramsholt church warden would climb his church tower to see if the Rev. Canham was being rowed over, but if the weather was bad and he was not to be seen then the congregation was sent home.

Later one of the Waller family, who had been landowners in Ramsholt and Sutton from the medieval period, combined the Ramsholt church living with one at the workhouse near Ipswich. He was also rowed over by boatman Button to a long vanished jetty near Shottisham Creek. He appears in the end to have got the living of Waldringfield and then Ramsholt was combined with Bawdsey.

When Lorna Burr lived at Ramsholt Lodge, she clearly remembered the Rev. Allott Tighe-Gregory, the Irishman who held the Bawdsey living from 1848 until 1911. The Church of England was very proud of their oldest active priest, but the Quilters did not see him as part of their modern forward-looking estate and tried, unsuccessfully, to have him removed.

Lorna Burr recalled that this ancient vicar, who was well over ninety, had sometimes to be wheeled up the aisle in a wheelbarrow by his church warden. Lorna claimed the church tower, an oval one which is probably Saxon, was in such a bad state that the bell was outside on posts and was rung by a man lying on the ground. She also wrote that there were so many holes in the church that owls got in and took the prayer books for their nests.

45. Ramsholt Lodge house shortly before it was pulled down in 1962. No-one thought that these old houses would ever be wanted again.

The highlight of the year was when Quilter's steam yacht *Peridot* came up the river. All the children in the parish boarded at the Dock quay and went down to Bawdsey Manor for the day. The day ended with all the children being given a doll, made by the Lady's maids, but the agent's children didn't get one because they were not considered to be needy cases. Seventy years later, Lorna Burr still felt the pain of being the odd one out and having to return home surrounded by village girls with new dolls.

While walking to the school, Lorna and her sister used to give part of their dinner to the farm children, who were always hungry. Agnes Thain, who grew up at the Valley Farm, might have been one of those children. She wrote about her grandmother Ann, who had lived in the wooden shepherd's cottage on the heath between Ramsholt and Alderton. Apart from attending church she had been a largely unschooled lady. When Alderton was given a new Recreation Ground she discussed this new development with her sister Alice. Alice said 'Sister Ann, have you seen this new Resurrection Ground?'

'Sister Alice, don't you show your iggerance so' retorted Ann, 'it's called the Procreation Ground'. She was told that considering what young couples were doing there after dark, she had got the right name!

What these country people lacked in 'book learning' they made up for in their wonderful ability to work horses and look after flocks of Suffolk sheep. In Ramsholt there was a large family of Burches, horsemen and shepherds, who seem to have descended from one 'Ninety' Burch. It appears that sometime in the 1870s 'Ninety' was staggering home from the Dock Inn the worse for drink when on the Valley meadow he fell face first into a puddle of water and drowned.

After this, it was said that several people claimed to have seen him and that if you walked up the meadow to the Valley cottages at midnight you would meet the ghost of 'Ninety' staggering home. Local children were terrified of this path after dark. All trace of path and the houses have long since gone, so the ghost of 'Ninety' must now walk alone.

After the Burrs left, a Scotsman called Fraser took on the tenancy of Ramsholt Lodge and one of the Burchs was his shepherd. Once, when Fraser went to visit his flock of Suffolk 'ships' (sheep) shepherd Burch suggested that a runt, in Suffolk a 'pindly one', was eating as much food as the good sheep, but would never put on any meat so it would be worthless. Fraser saw the point and said that it should be killed and put in a hole. When Fraser had gone the shepherd's boy rounded up the runt for its demise. 'Don't be a dizzy fool boy' said old Burch, 'he knows how many sheep there are in the flock, but he will never know which one we killed. Go and find the best 'ship', we can eat that!'

Fraser stayed at Ramsholt Lodge until about 1922 when he announced to his men that with the fall in cereal prices it was impossible to make the light land pay and he departed back to Scotland.

East Anglian farmers had once referred to sheep as having 'golden hooves' because they put fertility into the land and the sale of wool was profitable. However, once Australia had been cleared of eucalyptus trees and opened up for sheep-farming, imported wool from there killed the demand for more expensively produced British wool. The sheep walks on the belts of acidic light land all along the Sandlings coast of Suffolk were simply abandoned and grew up with 'brakes' (bracken). Lord Rendlesham owned a large part of the sheep walks and decided the way ahead was forestry. The ancient Tangham Forest was expanded by planting up the heathland with fir trees. The tiny hamlet of Tangham, once a shepherd's farm out on the open sheep walks, was surrounded by a dark forbidding forest of fir trees.

Unfortunately Lord Rendlesham's Tangham Forest was burned down during World War I, but in 1919 the new Forestry Commission started buying up the East Anglian heathland for new state forests. Britain had been badly frightened during World War I when German submarines cut off the supply of cheap raw materials from the Empire. The Forestry Commission was started to provide a home-grown source of pit props for the coal mines. The lack of imported pit props had almost closed the coal mines, which would have cut off Britain's main source of energy.

In the nineteenth century the Sandlings villages of Sutton, Hollesley and Ramsholt would have been very similar places. Isolated groups of farms and cottages were dotted around a vast area of open heathland, but today they are totally different because of decisions taken by the land-owners in the past. Ramsholt melted away because the major land-owner there had no interest in its growth, but similar nearby villages expanded and changed shape.

In the 1880s, the Barthorpe family decided to sell their estate in Hollesley. It was bought by an association which set up a Colony College to train emigrants how to cope with a pioneering life in Canada, Australia and New Zealand. This 'Colony' later became part of the prison service and a new housing estate, Oak Hill, was built away from the old village centre around the Knoll, at the bottom of Fox Hill. In the late twentieth century Hollesley has

46. Mrs Knights in about 1903. She had spent all her life working in the Ramsholt Lodge house. Also working at the house were two other maids and two gardeners, while two boys were employed to keep the farmyards tidy and open the gates for the carts and wagons.

Sandlings Peninsula about 1835.

47. Bert Last pulling down some of the cottages below Ramsholt Church, 1969. There was never a road to these cottages, just a footpath across the Church field.

48. Jonathan on 7ft of snow at Ramsholt Church in the hard winter of 1987. During forty years in the parish the longest time this road has been closed due to snow is three weeks.

moved on again and because it has quick road links to the places of employment in the Woodbridge-Felixstowe-Ipswich triangle, new urban housing estates have started to pop up. The change of ownership back in the Victorian period led to Hollesley becoming the most populated village on the peninsula.

Back in the early years of the twentieth century, the Bawdsey Estate had slowly taken on more of the old Rendlesham Estate, but this stopped with Quilter's death in 1911. In 1914 the Rendlesham Estate sold half of Sutton village to the Pauls, Ipswich malsters who wanted it to entertain visiting German brewers pheasant-shooting. In the 1930s the council, in the first community effort to improve living conditions, started building new houses near the Bawdsey-Woodbridge road and in the 1960s the Pauls began pulling down outlying cottages and building new ones, also near the main road, for their farm-workers. Thus, in the twentieth century, a village centre was created.

During the late Victorian Agricultural Depression people left the Suffolk villages and walked to the railway stations on their way to new lives in the cities. By 1891 there were 50,000 Suffolk-born people living in London and another 23,000 living in industrial northern counties. There were other groups that had left Suffolk to go to the British colonies, mostly Canada and Australia.

By the late twentieth century, more affluent people have returned to these villages, driving out in cars looking for houses to buy so that they can live in the countryside, but commute to the towns for work.

I was once rang up by one of the new residents, who had paid an inordinate sum of money for a barn conversion. He was in a steaming temper and said 'when I bought this house no one told me that there was going to be intensive agriculture going on in the field. I must meet you and get this stopped!'

I had some sympathy with the new barn-conversion owner, he probably had been led to believe his new home was set in a sort of rural parkland. In fact, although it did not affect him, he had bought a home in the middle of one of the most progressive agricultural areas in the world. One never knows whether to laugh or cry when talking to well-paid people working in technical advanced industries who go home in the evenings to the villages and think the fields around them should be worked in the eighteenth century manner.

Not long afterwards I took part in a conference to come up with a long term strategy for the Suffolk coastal district and one of the county planners tried to push through a policy of having 'farming phased out of the East Suffolk countryside because we didn't need it.' This naive and extreme view, perhaps encouraged by the bird empires which have taken over large areas of the coast, does not take into account there must be a balance. Food production, managed access, conservation areas and centre of population all have to exist side by side in the countryside.

Two Massey Harris combines behind Peyton Hall unloading barley into the Ford Thames lorry, 1951.

Joe North combining spring barley on Lodge Road, Ramsholt 1975.

Chapter Eight

GREY FERGIE TO MOBILE PHONE

LIFE IS WHAT HAPPENS
WHILE YOU ARE MAKING OTHER PLANS
John Lennon song

The countryside of my youth comprised undulating fields lined with elm-filled hedges and dotted with rambling farmhouses surrounded by a jumble of traditional buildings and horse ponds. The villages were plain and remote, living conditions appalling and the people crusty and independent. They were not in the least intimidated by centuries of being patronised by the squirearchy. Nor had Hitler's bombs shaken the old Suffolk people's ability to resist change and newcomers.

However, the United States Air Force unsettled everyone. Because they had a lot money to splash about, the Yankee servicemen drank all the beer and made off with the best-looking women. The countrymen found this very hard to tolerate, but the real eye-opener was the Americans' use of machinery. In East Anglia, where you were never more than five

49. Cutting wheat with a binder in 1995 at Felsham was a rare sight, but it was common until the mid-1950s. The wheat on Grandad's field, More's Farm, yielded 1,000 shuffs per acre, which was used to thatch the farmhouse.

miles from an American airbase, people became very aware that it was possible to have a better standard of living and a better income.

After World War II the Government put in place programmes to lift living standards in the countryside. They turned British agriculture into one of the most efficient industries in Europe, producing cheap and plentiful food, although mechanisation meant that fewer people were in employment.

Not everyone in the villages worked on the land, there were many other occupations, but the links with farming were close enough for everyone to understand what was happening in the fields around them. All this changed when living standards started to improve and the farm worker's wages rose each year. There was a desperate race against time to buy new machinery or some new technology to cut down the labour requirement.

The most labour-intensive crop was sugar beet. In the 1950s we used to 'chop out' the sugar beet every spring with hand hoes. This was a very monotonous task and to speed it up it was paid on 'piece work', so much a chain. I used to try and keep up with a gang of twelve men, moving slowly across the field with the steady chopping noise of hoes striking the ground. We were impressed that the nearby larger farms of Mann's and Paul's often had gangs of well over twenty men moving in a line across a field, hand-hoeing beet.

While we were hand-hoeing there was nearly always a steady conversation going on in the line of men walking forward with their heads down. As I remember it, this was usually spicy village gossip about such subjects as which boy and girl had been spotted the night before heading for the bottom of Alderton Allotments. Also, a gamekeeper had an affair with a lady from the village out in the shepherd's hut on the marshes and this was a source of endless speculation. In the close-knit and often down-right nosy village community nobody could have any personal secrets.

In the autumn the sugar beet were harvested. First the ground had to be loosened so that the beet could be pulled out by hand and it then had the tops sliced off with a sharp hand tool known as a 'nopper'. Before it reached the factory the beet was handled by hand, nopping and forking, up to five times.

To try and speed-up the sugar beet 'campaign' a primitive machine called a spinner arrived at Manor Farm in about 1957. The idea of the spinner was that it spun the beet out of the ground and left them in neat rows for the hand 'noppers'. Only it did not quite work like that, because the spinner kept bunging up. I drove a 30hp Fordson Major tractor with the spinner on the back while our poor old horseman Walter Halls walked along behind with the 'nopper', pulling out the beet before it blocked up. After a few years an even better tool called a sugar beet sledge arrived, but even then the beet still had to be topped by hand. No wonder the farms required such a massive labour force, but so long as the money was there to pay them no one worried how many men they employed.

When a small army of people worked on the farms very little overtime was done by the whole workforce except at harvest time. Even with two combines we had to keep them going for as many hours as possible. I drove a combine to fill in at meal times and when the normal drivers were busy elsewhere. It was a dirty, dusty, noisy job, but it gave tremendous satisfaction, cutting through the standing corn and watching the golden grain pour into the trailers. Pearl often brought our young family up on to the harvest field for a picnic. The sweet smell of freshly cut straw on a hot summer's day is always a pleasure. As a child she had been to the harvest field with her mother, but her father at that time drove a binder. The harvest techniques have changed, but the rhythm of country life is continuous.

All our farm buildings had been laid out for hand labour and horses and carts. The story

50. The old Ramsholt shepherd's hut used to store pheasant food. The shepherds lived in moveable huts out in the fields during lambing time.

passed down by word of mouth from the Victorian times was that the Manor Farm buildings were built of bricks made in the 'kell' (kiln) at one end of the farm, while the cartsheds were actually built with timber cut down from the hedgerows and thatched with reeds cut by Bawdsey Fleet. These traditional buildings had a wonderful homely feeling, they belonged in the landscape, but they were quite useless in the new mechanised age.

Although we were primarily a dairy farm, the dominant sound was not the gentle lowing of cattle, but the steady crunch of a cement mixer as the buildings were adapted for tractors. Our first new building, a grain store at Manor Farm, went up in 1956 and we were putting up new buildings or enlarging the old ones until the milking parlour was built in 1972. Most of the neighbouring farms went further and pulled down the majority of their traditional buildings, but we held back and decided to keep some of ours. Since then I have struggled to find ways to adapt traditional buildings to justify saving them. The economics of the countryside are very harsh and however attractive a building, it will not survive unless it has a purpose.

About 1965 some of our Bawdsey herd of Friesians were entered for the Dairy Show in London and extra effort was needed to get them in peak condition. We used to mix all our cow meal, ground by a hammer mill, in the Manor Farm barn, but someone suggested that the cows' coats would looked brighter if they were fed rolled barley. I was told to fill up some sacks with barley and take them in to Eastern Counties Farmers' roller mill in Commercial Road, Ipswich. On the face of it, not a very difficult afternoon's work.

I loaded about one ton, in odd-sized bags, on to our 7-ton Bedford lorry and set off for Ipswich. At the mill they were busy and I was shown where I could unload the bags. The very last bag was a small one at the front of the lorry and carelessly I half bent down and picked it up without bending my knees. At once there was a sharp pain at the bottom of my spine and although I did not realise it, my life was just about to take a turn for the worse.

Driving home, I was in terrible pain with sweat running down my face. I had done my back a serious injury and was in various degrees of pain for over ten years. At times I could hardly walk. I was then married with a young family, and was a partner in the farms. I had wanted to have my own farm, but once when I put in a tender for a small farm on an estate

79

the agent told us that over seventy people had applied. Even if I had got it, I doubt whether the 120 acres of heavy land could have provided rent for the landlord and an income for Pearl, myself and three young children.

Instead, I went into partnership with my father and at the time I was not very proud of it. Looking back, I can see that this was the new era of farm management. Agricultural holdings had become large and were turning into businesses which would last longer that one man's life.

I suffered from frustration at being unable to do manual work with the bad back. In my mid-thirties the back trouble steadily cleared up, but long before this a doctor had suggested to me that I should get 'another string to my bow', so that I didn't have to go back to the heavy manual labour.

I started writing to kill time when I was laid up and some of this was drawn to the attention of James Wentworth Day, then a renowned writer on rural East Anglia. Wentworth Day became very enthusiastic about my country tales and as he was the editor of the *East Anglian Life* magazine he commissioned me to do a series of articles. The first time I actually saw the great man he was standing on Maldon's historic Hythe Quay in plus-fours and aiming a huge shotgun at imaginary wild geese flying overhead. This really summed him up, a romantic dreamer obsessed with shooting and history.

Wentworth Day, through his writing, all written in long-hand with an ink pen, had fought a single-handed campaign to keep alive the East Anglian country order of the nineteenth century. He had no time for the Welfare State and believed passionately that the countryside should still be run by the squirearchy; the land-owners who invited him for a day's shooting got particularly high praise. He believed that farmers, farm workers, gamekeepers, wildfowlers and poachers were the salt of the earth and the very foundation of our civilisation. Although never one to let the facts get in the way of a good yarn, he wrote about the old rural order with great skill.

Since I had been working on a farm since I was fifteen most people dismissed my early attempts with a typewriter, but Wentworth Day encouraged me and I doubt whether without his (and Hervey Benham's) encouragement I would have gone on through the long learning process.

Wentworth Day did not drive a car, so once I found myself driving him out for a highly unusual evening in rural Essex. First we drove through 'Keep Out' notices to Abberton Reservoir to look for wildfowl, Wentworth Day was convinced that the manager was a great personal friend of his. The evening ended in a village pub where he had instigated an annual dinner to celebrate the appearance of a ghost. The ghost had never shown up at any of these events, although several rural gentlemen had a fairly good evening's drinking and waiting in expectation.

In time I learned to keep farming and writing very separate, but to start with I did quite a lot of agricultural journalism. It was tremendously intriguing to find out how totally differently these two fascinating ways of earning a living were treated. No-one cared what farmers thought, but since their businesses had large spending power there was a massive publicity industry trying to influence them. On the other hand, everyone cared passionately about which way a journalist's sympathy leaned. They were plied with reasonable food, plenty of drink and even at times correct facts in order to sway their thoughts.

Up until the end of the 1960s agriculture was simply mechanising the traditional farming methods used before 1939. The same number of men was employed, but they worked a shorter week for far higher wages. At the end of the 1960s mechanisation suddenly began to go up another gear and tremendous changes were on the way. At the time our predominantly light land arable farming was not paying, but the Bawdsey dairy herd was keeping us going.

When Pearl started doing the wages in the early 1960s there were thirty-seven men on the regular payroll and several more men and women who worked on a casual basis harvesting vegetables. We had our own cricket team and a major local event was the match against the neighbouring farms run by the Mann family, and no quarter was given on either side. Once we won spectacularly, thanks to some outrageous umpiring by our Bob Barker.

Everyone began to develop their dairy herds, so there was soon massive over-production of milk and the returns dropped. We overcame this by mechanising the way the cows were milked. In 1972 a new yard and milking parlour was up. This meant that instead of three men milking eighty cows in a traditional cowshed, two men were able to milk 130 cows. The new buildings were a dream, for both men and cows, compared to the Spartan conditions of the long open cowshed. But all the time the price of milk was failing to keep pace with the rising wages and costs. There had been about twenty herds around us, but one by one they were sold off. By 1980 the only milking herds left on the Sandlings peninsula were Quilter's, Hollesley Colony's and ours.

At the time several experts tried hard to advise me that if the herd size was doubled then it would return to profitability. With the Sandlings, extra low rainfall we were in the wrong part of the country for grassland farming. If we had doubled the herd size then all the water available for irrigation would have had to be used on grass rather than on more profitable

51. 'Joe' North driving a Claas combine cutting spring barley beside the Lodge road while 'Sid' Spall of Shottisham watches out for rabbits about 1975.

vegetable crops. The decision to get rid of the Bawdsey herd of 130 dairy cows was undoubtedly the hardest I have had to take. Not only had my father spent his life building up the herd into a really worthwhile collection of cattle, but the jobs for all the men who looked after the herd and their followers also went.

When I broke the news that the herd would have to go to the head herdsman, John Webster, he said 'It's obvious you are losing money, we had worked that out, and I am surprised you've gone on so long.' All this happened nearly twenty years ago, yet a lump still comes to my throat when I look at the former cattle yards.

At that time, many experts were predicting great changes, but no-one was certain what these changes were going to be. Once at a conference at Cambridge in 1970 an expert on the dairy industry told us that British farmers simply had to wake up and get their act together because agriculture, under the communities in eastern Europe, was making such progress forward that we would soon be swamped by their cheap milk and beef. He had just been taken on a tour around the massive collective farms of Eastern Germany and had fallen under the spell of the 'big is beautiful' propaganda. Communism was the great red herring of the twentieth century, a system that sounded good in theory but in practice turned into ineffective corruption.

It was not until 1983, when I journeyed through the sandy lands of East Germany that I found that it was as I imagined Victorian England had been. The villages were run-down and scruffy, while out in the huge open fields shepherds and their long-haired dogs stood all day; even in the rain they just wrapped themselves in huge capes, watching over their flocks. It looked wonderfully biblical, but their massive wage bills made their agriculture sink further and further into the red until the collective farming system collapsed.

I switched to potato growing as our main line, but being in a remote place I always had great difficulties in finding enough people to come and pick up the potatoes by hand. We did have our loyal gang of local ladies, who came every year and worked at a steady pace, although I often wished they would go a bit faster. The other half of the gang changed most years and was made up of people who wanted to earn some money, but found the manual work in the fields a profound shock.

My two gangs never mixed and seldom spoke, but both sides accused me of giving them the worst areas to pick. The only time I had serious trouble was when one of the visiting potato-pickers made an offensive remark about another picker's West Indian husband. Our loyal country ladies just went on picking up potatoes as if nothing had happened, while the others divided into two camps and started fighting like wild cats. By the time the police arrived there were young women bleeding and sobbing all over the field.

For most of year, the farm was 'male only' and everyone rubbed along happily enough, but when the women arrived for the early potato season the atmosphere became electric with all sorts of mild flirtations and rivalries springing up. Some men behaved like lion kings defending their prides.

The women were then paid less than the men, but didn't lift the bags, the heavy work was always done by the men. Then came the day when everyone was paid the same. The men were furious and said equal pay, equal work and the women should lift their own bags. The women were angry and genuinely bemused, and I had to say that the law did not allow me to define this as a 'woman's job' and this as a 'man's job'. The local ladies left, in fact most of them were of retirement age, while the younger women said they were just as strong as the men and would lift the bags. However, they found it hard and only a few stayed with us.

The farm's working day began at 7am. First of all I met the gang of men at Peyton Hall in a dilapidated Victorian riding stables. This building did not have electricity so that at 7am in the winter I used to walk into total darkness and had to recognise voices which said 'morn Robert', to know who had turned up for work. We then planned the day's work without actually seeing each other. My routine was to drive to the Valley Farm next, again no lighting, but by this time it was a little bit lighter and I could see the features of the four or five men leaning against the pillars of the open dirt-floored Victorian cart-shed. On a really dark winter's morning I would discuss the day's work with about a dozen men without seeing any of them.

One of the great rituals on the farm was the 9am 'ninzes' break. The whole farm stopped dead and then there was another brief stop at 11am and 'dinner' at midday followed by 'threezes' at 3pm. Basically the work stopped roughly every two hours, as if the long-gone Suffolk horses were still being given a break. Only a few men did much overtime, the general principle was that if you wanted a job done quickly you took on more men.

My father's generation of farmers often complained bitterly that compulsory tractor safety cabs added to the cost of the machines without any advantages at all, but cabs created as great a change to farm working practices as the departure of horses. Many early metal cabs rattled so much that the drivers often took the doors and windows out, but once the manufacturers produced a more comfortable working environment men were happier to work very long hours during busy periods. The 'Q cabs' provided warmer conditions and the work was done by fewer people. However, the transition period was not smooth. There was rivalry between drivers with and without cabs. Since money was only available to change one or two tractors after a good harvest, it took a decade before the last of the old open tractors went.

52. Potatoes for the early market being lifted on Lodge Gate field, Ramsholt Lodge Farm in 1981.

During the potato harvest of June and July my day started at around 6am when the merchants phoned and there was a lot of haggling over the price for that day. This was a challenge, but demanding. We had problems with some of the hand-pickers and the lorry drivers trying to pack on more potato bags than they had signed for, making it a long day.

In 1980 I tried to simplify the system by buying a Grimme Command harvester which took the potatoes out of the ground and along traces into bags. At the time I thought this German machine was the answer to a potato grower's prayer, as seven men could harvest the same tonnage of potatoes as the twenty-two hand pickers. The next year I bought another machine and now was employing our regular men and a few students to man them. Some of the students were very good and came for several years. Others were used to sitting around at universities having discussions on world problems and saw the potato field as a good place to continue the Marxist struggle against the capitalist classes. All I wanted to do was get the lorries loaded at the end of the day. I did not have time for long discussions on the moral position of the world's workforce! Our few student protests were done in the name of Communism, yet it was the collapse of that experiment which has provided us with the best seasonal workforce we ever had. In the late 1990s young people from Poland and other places in eastern Europe work hard and long for the 'good wages'. They come from a very real world.

The peninsulas between the Suffolk estuaries have a unique 'maritime climate'. It does not feel any warmer, in fact most of the time the cold sea winds make it feel colder, but because of the high salt content in the air the frosts are not so severe, and the soil stays warmer so that spring growth comes earlier than in most of England. Also, in the autumn the growing season lasts slightly longer.

Potato growers were the first to exploit this slight advantage to capture the high prices on the 'early market'. The competition was always fierce, this was not just for high prices but there was a considerable 'one up-manship' in the district to be the first farm 'lifting' new potatoes.

We had a few sheltered fields near Peyton Hall which just caught the spring sunlight, providing a good place to grow early potatoes. There was a lot of hard work and expense during the winter putting the potatoes into trays so that they 'chitted', started growing, before they went into the ground. All the other growers were doing this too, so I looked for some other way to make potatoes grow faster and get the early market. In 1981 I decided to grow them under plastic sheets, something only two other growers in the eastern counties were trying.

The whole exercise was fabulously expensive and I watched with apprehension as the two fields vanished under a carpet of plastic. Then came a wild March night with a heavy rain and gale. We were on a learning curve and had not realised that stones could prevent the plastic from gripping the soil. To my complete horror, in the 22 acres we had done on a stony field near Ramsholt Church, some of the plastic had blown out. The sheets were flapping wildly in the wind, while others had come off completely and were wrapped around the hedgerow. It was not a pretty sight and took Mo Malster and Ron Webb the whole weekend to salvage most of the plastic with shovels and put it back on by hand.

The idea was to put a whole field under a greenhouse effect so that the soil temperature rose. Under these conditions the Ulster Sceptre potatoes grew faster and we lifted loads early and sent them off to the London markets for the high prices. Shortly afterwards two curious officials from the Potato Marketing Board arrived on the farm to find out just what we were up to. These were the first potatoes lifted in the British Isles that year. The advan-

53. Taking plastic off carrots at Walk Barn field, Ramsholt in 1981. This was then a labour-intensive operation.

tage was short-lived, because the next year all the leading growers had plastic sheeting as it was quickly realised that as the crop was lifted sooner, then a second crop could be planted.

Part of the reason for increasing our potato-growing activities was the mistaken belief that I had a responsibility to find employment for the remaining fifteen men left on the farm after the cows went. I had steadily increased our potato acreage so that they had become our major investment. This worked well until the bumper crop of 1985 which glutted the market. We sold a few tons, but lifted several fields at a heavy loss and many unsold tons were dumped in pits. Since the money to pay the men's wages through another year would not be there, I made twelve men redundant on the afternoon they harvested the final field. Many of these men I had worked with and alongside over the past thirty years. This was heart-breaking for all concerned.

I had delayed laying off the men for a long time, too long, but I discovered I was not in isolation. Although I did not find out until later, on the same day as I had given most of our men their redundancy notices two large estates on the peninsula had halved their workforce. At this period, in the fifteen villages on the peninsula between the rivers Deben and Ore, at least 300 regular farm jobs vanished. The men who remained were far better rewarded than their grandfathers would have ever dreamt.

Each purge meant fewer people working on the land, but we didn't actually make any more money, simply stayed in business. Between 1984-94 the number of farmers and farm workers in Suffolk alone fell by 2,500. The true human price of bringing down the cost of food in the shops.

This great social upheaval can be traced in the number of tractors we needed to work 1440 acres. In 1980 we had twenty-three tractors with an average of 55 horsepower. This meant more tractors than drivers, but because of breakdowns we kept just a few spare ones. In 1982 I cut this down to fourteen tractors with an average of 68 horsepower. Since I sold all the old tractors in one lot, some wag lined them all up in the farmyard and put up a 'sale of the century' notice. These were all tractors driven by the back wheels, which lose a great deal of their power. By 1999 we had three tractors of an average 115hp, but more important, all these had four-wheel drive which develops more power.

One of our tractors which escaped all this was a 1952 grey petrol/TVO Fergie which was left because it had no second-hand value. Anyway, I rather liked it and the Fergie remained abandoned in the corner of a barn for over twenty years, then after fitting new leads, distributor cap and battery it amazed everyone by starting at the third attempt and now has a new lease of life running a generator at harvest.

By the 1970s the whole western world was getting much more proficient at producing food, but the United States was determined to dominate the world market. The United States was putting great pressure on the European Economic Community to cut back the amount of grain it produced to make way for their increased production in the mid-west. The European Economic Community agreed to put some of its arable land into non-productive 'Set Aside', in which the farmers produced nothing, which was disheartening enough, but also meant a drop in their income. The GAT agreement went further and limited the amount of cereals Britain could export. A surplus built up quickly, and so too did public resentment, and it was predicted that cereal prices would drop.

I had costings undertaken which showed that if the price of wheat dropped from about

54. Three new Marshall tractors arriving at Manor Farm in 1983. Pearl, Robert, Richard Andrews, Jonathan, Ron Webb, Nobby Burch, Paul Burch, Doug Stanard, Brian Andrews and Peter Ransby, who were some of the farm's workforce at the time.

£110 per ton down to the predicted £82 then we would go out of business. Naturally, this led to a sharp intake of breath followed by a new farming policy in which only five men were employed. This new system appeared to be working well until salt water got into one of our irrigation pumping points and the irrigation water unwittingly destroyed a £70,000 field of over-wintered carrots. At the time this was big bucks and the loss had a major impact on the business.

Cereal prices did not fall at this stage, but stayed the same. However wages and all other costs continued to rise. We were being squeezed and forced to make further cut-backs. In 1988 we gave up cereal growing, laid off four men and just my son Jonathan and myself did potatoes, sugar beet and a few other crops.

The cereal land which went into Set Aside was laid down to grass and we now started a regular programme of grass-cutting, which we continued seven days a week throughout the summer. All this turned the tide of events back in our favour, but it was a very heavy workload for Jonathan and myself. In the summer we employed some outside help and Pearl joined in with the summer grass-cutting.

Pearl had for many years been doing the farm's accounts and general book-keeping. When she had lived on her father's farm she had driven his grey Fergie and had secretly harboured an ambition to plough as well as her father had done. When our daughters heard that their mother was, at an age when most ladies were moving into a comfortable retire-ment, actively cultivating large fields in a high-powered tractor they rang up to protest that this was not a good idea. Pearl was very disappointed when I talked her out of ploughing.

We have two daughters. Caroline always liked the farm, but I believe has been far happier with her career in the ever-changing world of fashion design, as well as getting married and having two children. Joanna was never much interested in the farm, but she was the one who married a farmer, Simon Garrod from Felsham.

When I left school and started work on the farm I don't remember anyone bothering to ask me if that was what I wanted to do. Actually it was, but I told Jonathan that he did not have to come on the farm, the decision was his, but this had the effect of making him keener.

With Jonathan and I working the farm we would get up just after 6am, have a cup of tea, and then go out for a day's work. On 16 October 1987 we were up at 5am, because a wild wind was shaking our timber-framed house. Being an old house the windows did not fit all that well and the pressure of the wind kept forcing them to fly open. In the end, we got a cord and bound the windows.

After our early morning cup of tea, before going to see the men, I said, 'You know we had better take your tractor because after this wind there might be a tree down on the Lodge road.' This was the understatement of my life. As we rounded the corner there was not one tree down, but hundreds. We stood in amazement looking at the devastation caused by the tail-end of the hurricane which had passed through our parish a couple of hours ear-lier. Had the hurricane come a little later we, and many other people in the district, would have been out and on the roads and there would have been loss of life.

A very wet autumn had made the ground soft and many trees still had their leaves on. Hit by the strongest wind in south-eastern England for 250 years, the trees just rolled over. Overnight the landscape completely changed. Where the day before there had been lovely woods, now there were just a few trees sticking out of a tangled mass of branches and bro-ken tree-trunks. I was very sad to think that I would never see our parish full of woods again in my lifetime. I thought perhaps I should plant trees for the future

Greg ploughing on the Channel field, 1993

Jonathan drilling winter wheat on the Bluecoats field, 1993.

Chapter Nine

FARMING IN THE FAST LANE

DRILL INTO DUST AND COME UP IT MUST
DRILL INTO SLOP AND GET A GOOD CROP
Old farming saying

The summer of 1992 was long and hot. Wonderful to go outside every day into hot sunshine, but on light land near the Suffolk coast where the rainfall is the lowest in Britain, it was fairly disastrous for farming. Our most important job was to keep the irrigation going on the sugar beet. We did this seven days a week, often one of us getting up at dawn to start the irrigation reels off and at the end of the working day changing other reels. Pearl and I spent several Sundays carrying irrigation pipes through wet waist-high sugar beet, sometimes glancing longingly down at the boats sailing on the river and wishing we were there.

Such hard work appeared to be rewarded, because by the end of August Wallpond and Topstackyard fields, over 50 acres of sugar beet, looked superb. A few years later a similar crop on a neighbouring field yielded 26 adjusted tonnes an acre (64 tonnes a hectare) and the factory told us that one week our beet had the highest sugar content of any beet lifted in Britain. Then one day when I arrived at Topstackyard on a tractor to move the irrigation reel I found two men from the Ministry of Agriculture loading samples of the beet into the backs of their cars. A few days later I received a very serious phone call from a Ministry man breaking the awful news that those two fields had rhizomania. This soil-borne disease, which had possibly entered the country on the soil of vegetables for the supermarkets, had come from southern Europe and the Ministry were attempting to stop it from spreading in Britain. I was ordered to destroy the crop at once, without compensation, and was told we would not be allowed to crop those fields again. The fields had to be put down to grass and we were not allowed to even walk on them.

At that time sugar beet was our main earning crop, so this was a major blow. It really hit me the day I went into the fields to destroy the crop by discing it up. As the beet were torn out of the ground and crushed I wept at the lost effort and income. In fact, rhizomania was found throughout the light land farms of East Anglia and the Ministry were forced to rethink their containment policy. The National Farmers' Union, bless them, had a scheme which paid us some compensation, keeping the bank off our backs, but every cloud has a silver lining and we were forced to rethink our farming policy.

With Ministry regulations taking these fields out of our rotation we had to find more land to grow beet on in the future. A chance meeting with Herman Simper, one of my Charsfield uncles who had retired but still owned some fields, gave us an opportunity to rent some future fields for sugar beet. But these fields were some seven miles from our main holding at Bawdsey.

We discovered, as had many of our neighbours on the Suffolk coast, that the present generation of tractors with fast gearboxes were only slightly slower on the road than much of the other traffic. In fact, distance was not a problem and we could farm land miles away.

Jonathan bought mobile phones, then a very novel invention, in 1992. The first mobile

55. Frank Ling doing some nostalgic sugar beet 'nopping' in 1980 with a sugar beet harvester in the background on Cliff Hill field. Frank had retired four years before, but thought he would like to do a piece of beet by hand. In 1990 Fred Garnham with 2 acres was the last small grower to have a contract with Ipswich Sugar Beet Factory and the last person to completely harvest his beet by hand.

56. Harvesting sugar beet on Cliff Hill field in 1980. Gangs of men working by hand had long gone. By this time these three-row harvesters had been produced, but about five years after this photograph was taken sugar beet harvesters had increased in size and cost again so that individual farms could no longer afford to operate one. Contractors undertook the work on several farms.

phones were expensive and heavy, it was like carrying a brick around all day, but keeping in contact saved an enormous amount of time. Jonathan lost his first mobile during harvest, all he knew was that it was somewhere in the 22 acre Stackyard field we had just combined. It was literally like looking for a needle in a haystack. He took my mobile and at dusk drove around the field phoning his number until he heard a faint ringing under the barley straw. All the time we were learning new techniques!

About this time, thanks to the exchange rate and the pound falling in value, cereal-growing suddenly improved and we took on Greg as a ploughman and John as fitter/drill man, and stuck our necks out and borrowed the money to buy all new machinery to go back into large-scale wheat and barley growing.

All the time it was getting harder and harder for a small family concern to succeed. Since life is not perfect no farming system can be, we searched for a farming system which made a living for us without damaging the countryside. There was no set pattern, every farm around us operated in a completely different way.

I can't help thinking that the most successful occupants of the land on the Sandlings peninsula have been the rabbits. Over the past century they have been trapped, shot and gassed in their tens of thousands, to say nothing of surviving the horrible 'myxy' disease, yet they are still there nibbling away destructively. The rabbit's ability to breed at rapid speed is something we could not match, but they have another survival technique. It takes rabbits a long time to construct their warrens, they usually dig large main entrance holes, but as well as these they always have a back escape hole. This small hole, just large enough for a rabbit to squeeze through, is often under a bush somewhere behind the warren. When

57. Starting to drill winter wheat on Village field, Berghersh, 1997. This is our four-wheel steered Fastrac 1135 with a combi 4m power harrow, drill and a press on the front. Because of the weight the tractor is on wide flotation tyres which reduce soil compaction.

a fox or dog starts digging down the main hole, the rabbits make a quick and silent exit out of the escape hole. This works well with natural predators, although the old warreners I went with as a boy used to find the escape hole and put a net over it, before they sent their ferrets in, and the rabbits popped into the net.

The rabbits have a very good point, always have a second option. For a period we made a dairy herd and then potatoes our main income and after this I followed a policy of always having an escape route by having some income, but outside farming. Our first diversification outside agriculture was in 1990, but we were very limited as to what we could do by the tenancy of some of the land.

For over thirty years our farming business had been stuck in the old landlord and tenant system. In 1959 the Ramsholt and Shottisham part of the old Bawdsey Estate had been sold for £125 an acre, which included all the houses, buildings and cottages, to new owners who eventually wanted to have it farmed by a large national company. Naturally we did not wish to give the land up to suit their plans. In the 1970s the landlords' farm manager went around our farm telling our men which of them he was going to employ when he shortly took over our farms. This caused a minor drop in our farm staff's morale which soon picked up when the landlord dramatically parted company with this ambitious manager.

This long stalemate went right on throughout the 1980s when the vegetable boom, driven by sales to the supermarkets, began to increasingly dominate the area. I was acutely aware that our light land could not be economically farmed in the last decades of the twentieth century without effective irrigation systems. My requests in writing to develop the property with a better irrigation system were fudged off, and then totally ignored. At one point I went for four years without meeting any of the landlords' agents, apart from a young, smartly-dressed man who got stuck in brambles while trying to hide from me.

We had dug our heels in and the next stage was for the landlords to start complicated legal arguments to try and prove that we had broken the leases. Our agent was always very keen for us to be aware that he had a letter on file stating that the legal disputes, real or not, would go on until the costs broke us. As this failed, we went to arbitration which the landlords believed would force the rent up. The arbitrator instructed them to give us a rent decrease. The landlords were thunderstruck, first by the drop in rent and then by the heavy legal bills, theirs and ours, which they very reluctantly had to settle. We felt the tide had turned in our favour and we decided to squeeze them until the pips squeaked.

Up until this stage it had cost the landlords a great deal and they were nowhere near achieving their objective. They replaced their long-standing agents and the newly appointed agent tried another approach. He offered cash for us to leave his clients' land completely. Since my father's old style tenancy could run for three generations, we felt we were in a strong position. Besides that, both Jonathan and myself loved living in this beautiful remote spot near to our boats and we said nothing would persuade us to move. Some things are worth more than money can buy.

Long months of silence followed, but we knew these negotiations were about to become very serious and would affect the next stage in our careers. Back came a series of offers which we rejected, our agent became alarmed. Pointing out that arable agricultural was in a buoyant position, if we stuck out for too much and farm incomes slumped again (which they did) then the landlords' offer would drop. The only danger we could see was that we would continue to be tenants of a thousand acres for about the next sixty years. We did not consider this to be much of a threat.

In 1995, both sides reached an agreement. We would give up renting some 800 acres, but become outright owners of 150 acres. This included the houses we lived in, which were very important to us.

This was sorted out in the spring, but in the autumn when the written agreement arrived it was not the same document that we had agreed in the spring. The landlords appeared to think that we would sign anything just to get out of the farms. Obviously some brinkmanship was going to be involved.

One foggy autumn morning, a well qualified and able young man, representing the landlords' agent, arrived at my door confidently expecting to put up the boundaries of our new holdings. I said that he had better come in as we had no intention of signing the revised agreement. He appeared surprised, someone had misjudged us again. Pearl made us all a cup of tea and we sat down around our living room table.

We explained we would not be signing their revised agreement and to back up the point I slid a cheque for the next six months' rent across the table. It was like Long John Silver tipping someone the Black Spot. The pleasant young agent's face dropped a mile, he shrank back in horror from the dreaded envelope and would not accept it. Jonathan and I glanced at each other and knew that this man could not leave the house without reinstating our terms.

When we eventually signed the final revised Buy-Out agreement our position changed. The professional advice was to use this little nest-egg to take early retirement, I have never met an agricultural adviser who advocates expansion. For us to retire sounded unchallenging and we were further influenced by the fact that Jonathan and Clare had just had a son, Harry. Our policy was to continue, we were the last of the Simpers from the Charsfield line to be running our own farming business. To the rest of the world that meant nothing, but we enjoyed our way of life.

We had two really exciting years acquiring more land and building up a new holding. It seemed as if we had spent more time in agents' and solicitors' offices than on the fields. It was very difficult to purchase a whole farm because land agents, keen to get the most money for their clients, split up farms and were selling them field by field. We bought and rented small areas of land, wherever available, in East Suffolk. When my father took on Ramsholt Lodge in 1950 the far end of his land five miles away could be reached by tractor from the main farm at Bawdsey in an hour. In 1995 the revolutionary JCB Fastrac tractor could reach land twenty-six miles away in one hour.

In 1996 my son Jonathan and I bought part of the Berghersh Place farmland. Sitting in the solicitor's office to complete the final details of land purchased, Toby Pound pushed photocopies of the deeds across the table and remarked, 'you might like to look at these.' I flicked through the photocopies and got a jolt when I saw the signatures of Will and Morris Turner. We had bought seven fields which had once belonged to my mother's family, but inflation made the previous values meaningless. In 1937 Will had bought a 200 acre farm, but it was actually a small country estate complete with large country house, Berghersh Place, a small Swiss Cottage and two lodge cottages, for £2000. Some sixty years later that same estate would have been worth well over a million and we paid more for one acre that the whole place cost Will Turner. This is why land prices are high, it is the best long-term investment. They are simply not making any more land.

The history of Berghersh must be typical of many East Anglian holdings. The name, locally pronounced Bergh'sh, sounds almost Germanic but it appears to be from an old word for 'property'. It is on high ground a few miles north of Ipswich which has been inhabited for many centuries. There was an Iron Age settlement close to the farm buildings while there is also the moated site of the large medieval manor house. This is one of some 740 known moated sites in the county, mostly in the central High Suffolk area. The moats were dug between 1200-1340 and were more anti-thief trenches and a source of water than defences against warring raiders.

The medieval house was pulled down by the Meadows family who in the 1830s, no doubt with high rents from the rich wheat-growing estate, built the rather square white brick Berghersh Place. Even after the repeal of the Corn Laws the great land-owners continued to enjoy high rents until the disastrous harvest of 1879. After this, many of the old families found it very hard to adapt to the drop in income and sold off their land to keep maintaining their standard of living.

The Berghersh Place and the 200 acre farm were all that was left of the big estate. The big Berghersh house was in a bad state of repair and Will let it to Mrs Stoter as a children's home. He lived for a time in Berghersh House, a poultry farm near the moated site. For a few years he farmed the land, but then retired to Ipswich and let the farm to Mr Chapman. When in 1952 Morris Turner sold Berghersh he got £9200, which he considered a very good price because it was over four times as much as Will had paid for it fourteen years earlier. The land agent Michael Spear handled this sale, and like all others at the time it was assumed that the house, buildings and several cottages would just be thrown in with the price of the land. Some farmers avoided buying a farm with a lot of worker's cottages because they were expensive to keep up.

Phil Chapman sold the Berghersh farm and house to a London barrister, but when he decided to sell in 1995 the land agents suggested he would get more if the whole place was divided up into small lots, which is how we came to buy seven fields.

Two years later we heralded the down-turn in land prices when we put in a very low bid for some land at Pipp's Ford, Coddenham and got it. Then we were amazed to discover that we had bought part of yet another of Will Turner's farms. Joe Turner told me Will had not owned this one but had rented it from the Shrubland Park Estate and claimed to have had the first milking machine in Suffolk there.

By coincidence, I know the recent history of some of the land we farm, but it has all been cultivated for a very long time. The field system in the Gipping valley would have developed from a pattern started in the Iron Age period, although they only had tiny enclosures. The Iron Age people lived in family groups farming the land around them, a natural way of life. As they cleared the land, decisions on where tracks or boundary hedges were to run were fixed by agreement between heads of farming families.

By the time the Romans arrived, the landscape was being intensively farmed and has been ever since. Nearly two thousand years ago the Romans built a fort and settlement, Combretovivm, at Pipp's Ford to defend the crossing over the River Gipping. This valley was then the route through Suffolk to land beyond and still is, only now we have traffic on the A14, and the railway, instead of trackways for driving cattle.

There is a timeless quality about open ploughed land and I often think of all those countless generations who tilled the same land that we farm today. Like us, they must have worried about bad harvests, which to the early people would have meant starvation. Only the methods of cultivation have changed, all the same anxieties are still there.

About the time we bought the land at Berghersh I flew with Doug Deas over the Suffolk coast, which was the first time I had seen it from the air. Below us the fields and villages were spread out like an untidy map. It was a grey spring day and the weak sunlight glinted on the irrigation ponds which were dotted around the area. Then we passed over the two huge runways of the former USAF air bases and beyond that the carefully controlled bird reserves. The plane backed in a stiff breeze and we headed back to Ipswich Airport.

Irrigation ponds, air bases and bird reserves are twentieth century additions to the landscape. The houses and villages have been here longer, but are packed in tightly. This is the coast where the government wants to give up sea defences, which means that seventeen villages and towns will slide slowly into the sea. Unfortunately it is not possible to only defend them, because the sea can eat away on either side and get behind the towns. This is happening with Southwold and the land lost can never be replaced.

The relentless pounding of the soft Suffolk coast is a natural process, but doing nothing to prevent it is not a long term option. In the end south-eastern Britain will need to have all its coast defended against the sea and instead of losing valuable decades really needs to start immediately.

In Britain people are packed in at over six hundred to the square mile and perhaps that is not obvious on the wild shingle beaches of Suffolk. You have to go and see the way Greater London, north Kent and the East Midlands around Milton Keynes are steadily pushing the tide of bricks and cement over the green fields. Space on land and fresh water are some of Britain's most precious assets. There is no shortage of open sea on the world's surface.

As an endless tide of houses, roads and industrial estates rolls over the green fields of England the demand for the remaining fields grows even stronger. Since World War II land has never been sold at its real agricultural value, but there has always been a premium for its scarcity value. The premium varies according to the economic climate.

The expanding urbanization puts tremendous pressure on the remaining countryside and farming and wildlife are constantly forced into smaller and smaller areas. The massive removal of hedgerows that went on until the late 1980s was prompted by a desire to compensate for lost land. Perhaps the wide open fields of East Anglia don't look like the result of a land shortage, but they are. Everywhere new out-of-town shopping centres, golf courses and even bird reserves have put great pressure on the remaining farmland which is needed to produce food.

The controlled use of irrigation is one of the ways agriculture has made up for the loss of land. The reservoirs seen from the air are for water which is 'banked' for summer use. I thought of the first early attempts at irrigation over forty years before. The first people to have irrigation equipment in Suffolk were Jim Mann and my father. They bought it, not to improve crop yields, but to try and wash the salt out of the soil after the 1953 Floods. The second year they tried irrigating sugar beet and potatoes and the yields more than doubled.

Our first system consisted of twenty-three hand-moved sprinklers supplied with water pumped by a tractor from a marsh ditch. Everyone was astounded to see a small corner of a field being sprayed with water. Elderly farm workers from miles around arrived on their bikes to stand and stare at this latest new wonder.

In farming circles early irrigation soon became known as 'irritation', because there were so many difficulties with it and the operator usually finished the day soaking wet from leaking pipes. Since East Suffolk has a very low rainfall, often only about 24 inches a year (575mm), in the past many crops died because of the lack of rain in May and June. A small amount of water at the right growth stage turns a disaster into a satisfactory crop.

In the past, early harvested crops in Britain were either grown in the Channel Islands,

Cornwall or Pembroke. By the early 1980s the farmers on the Sandlings peninsula realised that the maritime climate on the Suffolk coast, coupled with irrigation, produced crops which could be harvested earlier than in most parts of Britain. Since this advantage only affects about twenty large farms no-one had made the progression on to becoming main packers supplying the supermarkets. In 1983 we grew early carrots for Fenmarc, a group with a packing unit in the Fens, and about this time the Suffolk coast started to become an outpost for the Fen vegetable packers. In the past growers had just grown a crop and then tried to sell it, but this has changed, so that now most crops are sold before they are grown.

London wholesale markets and canners once dominated vegetable growing, but the major supermarkets replaced them some time in the early 1990s and became all powerful. After the BSE beef health scare the supermarkets became paranoid about food quality, which is perfectly understandable, so any farm selling to supermarkets has to be part of an 'assured crop' scheme. The crop must be grown with as little chemical help as is economically possible, certainly no chemical which will be the slightest danger to health is allowed. This is all very commendable, but some supermarkets, if they can buy cheaply from overseas, happily sell food knowing very well that it was not produced under the same strict rules as we have in Britain.

Jonathan with the suckler beef herd on Manor Farm marshes, 1998. This pastoral scene seems timeless, but the countryside is constantly changing. In the nineteenth century the battle for the minds of men was between church and chapel, but in the late twentieth century it was between working farmers and those who saw rural Britain as being an environmental and amenity area.

Chapter Ten

THE WEATHERVANE

Put British Pork back on your Fork
Advertising slogan

In 1987 Chris and Jan Packard bought the old barn at Street Farm, Framsden from the Helmingham Hall Estate and had it converted to be their home. It was a successful barn conversion and later won an architectural award. The selling of this barn ended centuries of ownership by the big estate, as Street Farm appears to have been part of the Framsden Hall manor, which became Helmingham Hall Estate in 1520. This was a period when land occupation was going through one of its transitional periods.

In the medieval period the custom of land occupation deeded that a manor controlled an area of countryside and that some individuals, the copyholders, had the right to farm certain areas, but they had to pay the Lord of the Manor a set fee. Also, the Church took a tithe, a tax based on the old Roman law of the state having a tenth of everything produced. The copyholders were really subsistence farmers, growing enough to feed their families and made some form of payment to the Lord of the Manor. By the Elizabethan period the Lords of the Manor were becoming outright owners of the land, which they could then rent out to anyone. The new tenant farmers pushed yields in order to pay rent and at the same time provided more food to feed the people in the expanding towns.

58. The greyhound weather vane on Simper's Barn, Framsden, 1998.

The oak-framed barn and first part of the farmhouse at Street Farm were probably built sometime in the late Elizabethan period. The Helmingham Hall Estate must have been well rewarded for its original investment in creating this small farm. For around four hundred years Street Farm was let out to a long succession of rent-paying tenants. The only major expense occurred during the mid-Victorian period, when Lord John Tollemache rebuilt the farm buildings and extended the farmhouse. During this long period the farming techniques had changed so little that the tenants could go on using the same style of buildings. It was not until around 1957 that the Estate started to 'take in hand' its land and put much of it into one large enterprise run by their own farm manager.

The new mechanised methods did not require all the small sets of farm buildings and some were sold off. The Packards bought the Street Farm barn and builders moved in to convert it into an attractive home.

One day an elderly man walking past stopped and said to Chris Packard, 'that's old Mr Simper's barn and he thought a rare lot of his old greyhounds so you had better put the weathervane back'. Chris Packard put the weathercock in the shape of a greyhound back on the roof, called his new home Simper's Barn and thought no more about the subject for eleven years.

Then one day Jonathan and I had been into the centre of Suffolk looking to buy a JCB teleporter to load lorries. On the way home, I said, 'slow down as we go through Framsden and I will show you the little farm where our ancestors struggled to earn a living from the land for about 130 years'. We slowed down and there was Chris and Jan's home with our name on it, 'Simper's Barn'. After this we arranged a meeting. I imagined that as it was forty-three years since the last member of our family had left the village they would have been totally forgotten. However, Jan Packard knew the village's oldest inhabitant, Margaret Thurlow, and together we all set out to meet this lady. Going up a short lane and then walking through a garden to her Top Cottage. I frankly worried what family scandals I was about to unearth or perhaps, even more humiliating, she may never have heard of the family at all.

I need not have worried, Mrs Thurlow had known Fred Simper, but did not remember any details and suggested we ask her next door neighbours Basil and Marjorie Alexander for more information. They had just finished their mid-day dinner and it turned out that Basil had worked for the last member of the family to farm in the parish. He had worked for Herman, my grandfather Herman's nephew, who was the son of Fred William.

I remember my grandparents talking about this man, they always referred to him as Hermy, and that he was a 'poor old thing'. Basil Alexander said that his workers called him Hummy and said 'he was not a well man'. He appears to have come back to the Tollemache's Helmingham Hall Estate as the tenant of Southwood Farm. This farm is away from the main village and is on the high ground over a mile to the south.

When we visited Southwood in 1998 the farmhouse, a typical Suffolk 'high gabled' long house, had been 'sold away' from the land. The buildings were derelict, the barn was still standing but several other buildings were either collapsing or had already fallen down. This was unusual because after a decade of good prices paid for redundant farm buildings, the Framsden area was dotted with successful barn conversions.

It must have been very different when Hermy Simper had this 200 acre farm. He employed five men, engaged in 'mixed farming' which included a herd of just fourteen cows. In about 1937 the Tollemaches offered Hermy another 30 acres of land to farm and he went over to Charsfield in his little Morris car to discuss this business move with my grandfather. A short journey, but not without some hazards as the wheel came off on one corner and overtook the little Morris as it went bouncing along the country road.

My grandfather Herman advised him to take the land on. However Hermy was a cautious man and said another 30 acres would mean buying another horse and taking on another man and so managed to talk himself out of taking it.

Hermy Simper died aged fifty-four on Christmas Day 1954 and at his funeral at Framsden grandfather Herman thought this would be a good time to broach the subject of his son, another Herman Frederick (the farmer and agricultural journalist), taking on the Southwood Farm. Unfortunately, Grandfather Herman could not get near enough to Tollemache's agent in the graveyard and another farmer said to him, 'You are leaving it a bit late Mr Simper, waiting for the body to get cold before you ask for the land, it's already let.'

Everything had changed with World War II. Before the war, farmland was not valued very highly, but since then there have always been more people wanting to own farmland than there is land available. This was partly because agricultural holdings were expanding, but even more because so much land was being swallowed up by relentless urban development. Everywhere huge housing estates, industrial sites, business parks, golf courses and the rest rolled over into the countryside. Since about 1950 land values have had little to do with returns from farming, it has been sold at a premium based on the local scarcity value in the area.

The major change has been that in the past my ancestors were able to run their farms with a few simple cash books, while nowadays there is a mountain of paperwork and endless and usually pointless forms to be filled in. In the past the fields of England were full of men and women labouring away, but today there are as many people sitting in offices attempting to keep up with the pile of administration paperwork generated by agriculture. The land agency businesses have grown up simply to handle the administrative side and the seeking of permission from the ever-increasing number of authorities which control the countryside.

59. The weekly midday 'dinner' at Manor Farm has been partly a social family event and partly a business discussion. Robert, Pearl, Harry, Sara, Clare, Lilian, Jonathan and Norman, March 1999.

Being a farmer has always been an earthy and honest way to earn a living, and one of the delights of working in the countryside is to be surrounded by wildlife. It is very thrilling when you suddenly find yourself watching some small piece of natural theatre. Once a great north diver popped out of the water in front of me. I don't know who was more surprised, the duck or me. Another time I found a flock of exotic birds feeding on the marshes.

When I told my bird-watching friend he smiled politely and said 'You do realise you have just described flamingos', but that is what they were. Escapees from a zoo in Essex.

The natural order of life can be very cruel. As a young man, while moving irrigation pipes in a potato field, I saw a stoat pounce on an unsuspecting rabbit. The death screams of the rabbit are still with me. A few winters back Pearl and I witnessed a life-and-death chase between a fox and hare. The fierce gusts of a gale which blew clouds of loose snow across the frozen Pykles field caused the fox to lose sight of his quarry. Both animals dropped to the ground in the gusts, the snow clouds passed and the fox was slowly approaching its kill, when suddenly the hare put all its strength into a final dash for freedom over the hilltop. The fox stayed on the scent and the hunt continued off into the snow beyond.

Magpies, marsh harriers and foxes have all moved back into our area because another species, gamekeepers, have almost become extinct, holding out in just a few 'beats' where financial conditions are still favourable. Deer were probably here in the past, but they only returned after escaping from Campsea Ash and other parks during World War II. Badgers were brought from the edge of Greater London when a huge housing development enveloped their old home. Being urban badgers they did not take kindly to being dumped in the middle of a forest and sought out the nearest houses so that they could continue feeding from the dustbins.

I tried to help the wildlife by planting trees to fill up some gaps in woods and hedges. Most of these young trees died in the very hot summers of the early 1990s. Other young trees near a public footpath just vanished. Perhaps they now grace the corner of some small garden. The ones in isolated places had the tops eaten by deer in the winter. I felt like putting up a notice for the deer saying 'come on chaps, we're on your side, give us a break and let these grow. We're doing it for you!'

Perhaps the real message is that good intentions are not enough, conservation is another form of countryside management. A more successful wildlife conservation scheme was the returning of 100 acres of marshes, after thirty years of wheat, back to grass. This reached a stage in 1990 when we had a visit from the main committee of the Royal Society for the Protection of Birds.

They arrived in a large coach and we took them out on to the silent grass marshes, where there was a singing skylark per acre, apparently the maximum density. The RSPB spokesman Chris Durdin had brought out the committee to show them that it was possible to farm for wildlife in the same way as one would grow wheat or vegetables, but the message to the committee was that it costs money to produce a habitat for birds. This is really a very sad story because the rhizomania sugar beet disease, to say nothing of a need to boost income after the 1997 price collapse, resulted in us ploughing up the 100 acres of conservation grass. When the chips are down, charity begins at home.

Every year you set out to produce the perfect crop, in the spring there is a period of great hope and once or twice in a lifetime you get it right, exceeding all expectations. If you don't like the smell of damp soil or get a thrill every time a new crop breaks through the surface there is no point in being in farming.

After the Buy-Out deal we had halved our acreage, which was going against all the trends in agriculture where units were getting bigger and bigger. The advice to small acreage farmers is to use their land to diversify into other forms of income, which is another way of saying produce food as a hobby, make an income in some other way.

With the uncertainties of agriculture around 1990 we were forced to think seriously about some form of diversification and we started with workshops and storage. The most obvious form was to go into agricultural contracting, we already had the machinery and going to work on other farms helped spread the cost. We also tried such things as fattening oysters, which looked best on paper, but after three years too many of them died just before they were harvested. We learned that farming is not the only business which has its ups and downs.

The Lodge Farm Livery Stable was a good opportunity for Clare to use her skills with horses and the people who ride them. Also to adapt traditional buildings for a new use. Most of the older farm buildings had been built for horses so that, after a break of about forty years, horses returned to Ramsholt Lodge. Instead of the heavy harnesses of working horses hanging in the stables, there is the light tack of the riding horses.

Part of this new venture was adapting the open cart-shed to stables. Bert Scopes had told me that back in the 1930s they had used this cart-shed to hold their Harvest Home supper. Tables were laid out with food and drink to celebrate another harvest safely gathered in.

60. Jonathan and Clare putting the horses out to graze from Lodge Farm Livery Stables, 1999. Walking past the cart sheds adapted for riding horse stables

Since the days when a small army of men worked with horses and wagons on Ramsholt Lodge, food, in real terms, has become incredibly cheap. In the 1930s the average manual worker worked for an hour to earn enough to buy a loaf of bread. By the 1990s most people have only to walk in the door and hang up their coats and this time pays for a loaf of bread. This lowering of the cost of food has all been achieved with new developments.

How far to go with all the new techniques became a moral dilemma. In the late 1980s I gave up beef production for a while because I could not bring myself to use hormones to increase growth. Many American beef cattle are given stimulants to increase growth and the public there are happy to trust a new idea, but European food-buyers are much more suspicious. Although I worried about the effects of hormones getting into the food system I can see nothing wrong with using all the new varieties of wheat which are being developed, because at last we can grow a hard milling wheat to compete with North American grain.

There is very little hope that arable farming in Europe could seriously rival the wheat, maize and soya growers of the North American prairies. North America has a drier climate, very little environmental restrictions and much lower costs. There is no such thing as a 'level playing field' in world markets. Most developed countries find ways of protecting their agriculture and then dump their surplus on the world market, often at below cost prices.

61. Jonathan, Harry, Robert and Norman at Manor Farm, 1996 with our first JCB Fastrac 125. When Norman started buying tractors they did not have mudguards, when Robert started they did not have cabs, when Jonathan started they did not have suspension, goodness knows what Harry's generation will live to see.

In this highly competitive climate only the lucky and successful farming businesses have survived. The British Government, whichever major party was in power, was happy to subsidise some production costs to make food less expensive, but they were never interested in how agriculture was structured. The public just wanted a cheap and plentiful supply of food and if that meant large agricultural holdings, so be it. When Britain joined the European Economic Community their system was different. The EEC support payments were intended to keep alive the rural economy and small independent farmers.

Faster tractors, vegetable contracts and scrapping the farm tenancy laws have changed the Suffolk coastal area from independent farms into a huge chessboard, with large companies moving their cropping and machinery around. Once in the spring of 1998 we had our John Deere tractor out on a long contract planting potatoes at Ampton in west Suffolk, while to cultivate the fields near our house a tractor, driver and specialist de-stoner equipment from Cambridgeshire were hired. Those who are going to stay in agriculture are probably the larger units, so quite a bit of chess-playing is aimed at knocking out the other player's pieces.

The relentless onslaught of new technology has completely changed the countryside. The advent of the car has meant that people can live in the villages and work in the town, turning the country lanes into commuter routes. The new arrivals in the villages have come searching for an English way of life which has been under threat from so much emigration into the major cities. The new residents of the countryside have brought in different skills and ideas and brightened up rural life, but so many have come that 'Old Suffolk', the people born and bred in the villages, have become strangers in their own land.

The first public clash between town and country came with the new Labour Government in early 1998. New Labour, with its politics which made sense around the dinner tables of Islington, thought it would be popular to ban fox-hunting, abandon farming and turn the countryside into a huge recreational area for the urban population. In fact, to turn the countryside into a playground just as the rich had done in the past when they created private parks, model villages and planted ornamental trees.

I have no interest in fox-hunting with hounds or any other field sport, but Jonathan and Clare felt some form of protest should be made. Early in the spring of 1998 they lit a 'Countryside Beacon' and were delighted from their remote and wind-swept hill in Ramsholt to see four more fires on the skyline. Next they joined nearly 300,000 people in London for the 'Countryside March', which started off as a protest about banning hunting with hounds and expanded into the rural communities expressing the feeling that they were being discriminated against by the urban population.

Everything from the beef ban to the right to go angling was represented in the Countryside March. This was a peaceful demonstration and, as they cheerfully strolled through the streets of central London, Jonathan and Clare met several friends from all over the country. The Government was deeply shocked to find it was so unpopular and suddenly side-lined its proposed anti-hunting laws. This march really highlighted the widening gulf between the urban culture and old rural customs. The New Labour vision of the countryside as a relaxation area had not taken into account that fields and woods are places which people work in and care very deeply about conserving.

Everyone has the right to go into the countryside, but no-one has the right to go into it to make the lives of the people living and working there a misery. The footpath system is a good compromise between work, leisure and conservation, everyone loves the countryside, but you can love it to death.

The urban population does not think of the countryside as being an area where their food is produced. Everyone assumes that when the supermarket doors slide open they will always be crammed with food. They don't seem to relate the changes in the countryside to the ready availability of food. In the 1990s there is no world surplus of food, only the inability of politicians to distribute it to where it is most needed.

During the cereal harvest in August there is a real sense of achievement as every lorry leaves the farm loaded with enough grain to feed hundreds of people. In my lifetime wheat and cereal yields have risen from around a ton an acre to three or four tonnes an acres. Even with the loss of land from building this means East Anglia is producing at least four times as much food as it did in the 1940s.

In the early 1990s the curious EEC support payments favoured British farmers, but in 1997 the high value of the pound and collapse of Russian and Far Eastern markets saw grain prices fall like a stone. The year before, cereals had left the farm at around £107 a tonne, but our first load away that year was feed barley at £70 a tonne. The down-hill slide in agriculture started here and worsened and by the end of the summer we were selling wheat at £62 a ton. The effect was rather like jumping into a cold bath, a shock that does not do you any good.

62. Fred Garnham and Robert harvest 1998. This was taken in almost the same place as the photograph 35.

63. Left to right: Lady Marjorie Quilter, Norman Simper and Doug Deas, Bawdsey Fete, 1999. Lady Marjorie had just presented a gift from the village to Norman Simper to mark his retirement as Chairman of the Bawdsey Parish Council at Bawdsey. End of an long era, as he had been on the council for 52 years.

64. Simper Farms workforce, 1999. Robert with Labrador Belle, Pearl, Greg Garnham, John Leek and Jonathan. Greg was planting our potatoes on the Pykles with our 130 hp John Deere tractor after contractors on the same field had ridged-up and de-stoned the land.

The real blow was in the autumn when, for the first time in my life, sugar beet prices came down, but even then we were not as hard-hit as the pig producers, whose prices started to fall and went on falling for two years. Agriculture was in its worst financial crisis for nearly seventy years. This sudden change of fortunes took everyone by surprise as experts had been predicting three more good harvests and that by the millennium agricultural land would be in very short supply and be worth £5000 an acre. In fact, land prices were down to £2300 an acre, an indication of the drop in confidence.

The drop in farm incomes was bad enough for us, but this had a knock-on effect because agriculture is one of Britain's largest industries. Within two months of the first poor cereal prices, tractor and machinery firms were laying staff off. The same thing had happened in the early 1980s when dairy cows became scarce in the dry eastern counties. Most of the little firms which had supplied us just went out of business.

The collapse of cereal prices came at a time when I was turning more of the management over to Jonathan. It is a young man's world, although I have managed to hang on to the most comfortable chair in the farm office. Once Greg Garnham, our ploughman, as he chatted to Jonathan asked which machine he thought was the most important to the farm. Greg was wondering whether it would be one of the tractors, his John Deere tractor or the JCB Fastrac. Jonathan said the greatest asset was the computer used for the forward costings.

Growing crops is an expensive and risky operation and without proper forward costings you could not stay in business for long. The old farmers simply grew crops and then went to market to try and sell them, which worked well then, but now the crop tends to be costed out and sold before it is even planted.

As we struggled with costings to find a way to adjust to this dramatic and potentially disastrous drop in farm revenue, Jonathan said, 'you know, when you first came to Bawdsey as a small boy at the beginning of the war everyone was worried that one night German troops would land on the beach and come storming through the village. Nothing could be as bad as that'.

This historical perspective may well be true, but the biggest problems are always the ones that you are facing at the time. Time never stands still in the countryside, but the changes come slowly.

In 1999 Cambridge University produced a report saying that the small family farms would be swallowed up by the super agri-businesses. Nothing very original in this report because agricultural holdings have been getting steadily larger during the last two hundred years. However Cambridge points out that the whole process is speeding up and very large sections of the countryside will come under one management. Maybe they will be proved correct, but the future is very hard to predict because totally unexcepted events can render careful predictions useless. All I have done is to record how over the past two centuries we and our direct ancestors have bent with the winds of change to work our farms and their fields.

And that is the story so far.

[FAMILY TREE]

The first two generations of this family tree, Richard Simper of Framsden and Samuel Simper of Bedingfield, appear to be linked to the family, but this is a little tentative.

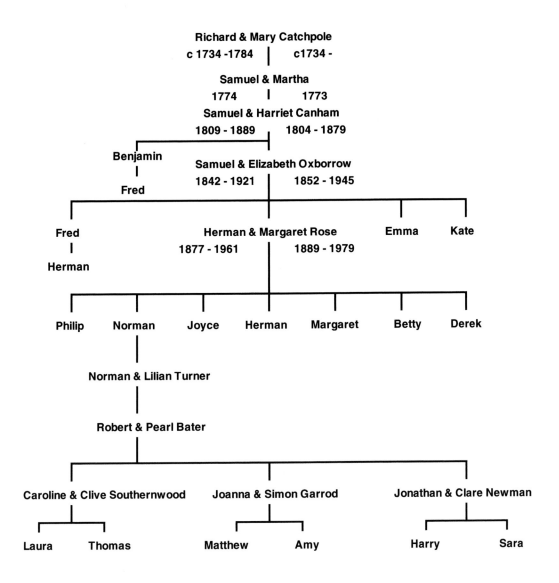

Some of the farms in Suffolk connected with the author's family.

GLOSSARY

BAIT. Animal food.

BINDER. The first mechanised corn-cutters, the mowers and then sail reapers, just left the unthreshed loose straw in a 'sworth' on the ground, but the binder also tied the straw into 'shuffs'.

BROADCAST. To spread seed on the land. In the nineteenth century this was done by hand while a Victorian invention called a Fiddle was also used.

CHOP OUT. Hand-hoeing sugar beet grown from natural seed so that there is a single plant about every six inches. Replaced in the 1960s by precision drilling with mono-germ seed.

COLDER. Husks and short pieces of straw taken out by a threshing drum.

COOMBE. East Anglian corn measure. Four bushels of cereals or half a quarter. With lighter corn only 12 stone of oats would fit in a coombe sack. A coombe of barley was 14 stone and a coombe of wheat was 18 stone. Farm men carried coombe sacks of wheat (114.3 kgs) on their backs up granary steps.

CROP MARKS. Lines of dark coloured crops marking the former sites of ditches and houses. The lines in crops made by tractor wheels are 'tram lines'.

COVERING. Mating a stallion with a mare.

DAG. Early morning dew.

DE-STONER. A machine which temporarily buries stones between the rows. This is because the vegetable harvesters can't tell the difference between stones and potatoes.

DISCS. Farm implement towed behind a tractor which has discs for cutting the soil. Used for soil cultivation, to chop-up straw and ground growth before ploughing.

DROSS. Suffolk word for corn unfit for sale.

FALLOW. Land left uncropped and ploughed to try and kill the weeds. In Suffolk 'Summerland' pronounced sumer'lond.

FASTRAC. British-built tractor with suspension and better braking for fast road travel. The next revolution after the Grey Fergie with hydraulic 3-point linkage.

GATT. General Agreement of Trade and Tariffs. One of the attempts at creating a level playing-field in international trading.

HAVELS. The sharp awns on the barley ears.

HEADLAND. Area of a field around the outside nearest the hedge.

HEAVY LAND. Strong clay soil which sticks to your boots.

LIGHT LAND. Sandy soil which can blow away in really dry weather.

MALSTER. Person in the malting trade.

MALTING BARLEY. Varieties of barley which make good malt. The barley is soaked in water and then when it starts to shoot it is dried and becomes malt.

MARSHES. Low land between the river wall and the rising land above sea level. Former rough grazing, but after the 1953 Floods this fertile land mostly went under the plough.

NOPPER. Sharp hand-tool used for cutting off the crown and leaves of sugar beet.

POLLY WIGGLES. Suffolk word for tadpoles.

RIVER WALL. Earth embankment to hold back tidal waters.

SEALS. Part of the harness of a working farm horse. The wooden seal fits on the collar which goes round the horse's neck. Always painted red with black tops in Suffolk.

SHEEP WALKS. Open areas of heathland, formerly used for sheep grazing, which were abandoned when Australian wool was imported in the nineteenth century.

SHOCK. A group of sheaves. They were built to let the bundles of cereal crop dry before they were carted back to the stackyard.

SHOCKING. Arranging pairs of shuffs upright in groups to make a shock.

SHUFF. Suffolk word for a sheaf or bundle of cereal crop before threshing.

STACK. Unthreshed corn or beans, straw, hay stored in the open pile. Victorian stacks were often rounded, but as yields increased they became large rectangles, but in East Suffolk a 'billyboy', like the type of sailing vessel, was rounded at each end.

STACKYARD. Pronounced stacky'd. Area where the stacks were built. Usually next to farm buildings.

STICK AND A HALF. Suffolk word for a flail used for hand-threshing corn.

SUBSOIL. Land just below the depth of the ploughed soil.

THRESHING TACKLE. The three units of a steam threshing tackle were the traction engine, the drum which did the threshing and the pitcher to take the loose straw up on the stack.

TRACE. Moving conveyer-belt of metal or rubber on a vegetable harvester.

TRACE HORSE. The leading horse when two horses were put on a wagon or tumbrel.

TUMBREL. Farm cart which loaded a ton and was pulled by a single horse.

20 shillings is one pound sterling
Three quarters of a sterling pound is perhaps one Euro
20 hundredweight (cwt) is one ton
Four and a half cwt is a quarter
8 stone is one hundredweight (cwt) or 950.802 kgs.
one stone is 6.35 kgs
2.471 acres is one hectare